Robert L. Herbert, Yale University   # NEO-IMPRESSIONISM

The Solomon R. Guggenheim Museum

Published by The Solomon R. Guggenheim Foundation, New York, 1968, Library of Congress Card Catalogue Number: 68–16803

Printed in Austria

INTRODUCTION

Art "isms" are stretched to refer at the same time to particular works and to esthetic concepts that have either been derived from these works or upon which the works themselves are based. In rendering such a double duty, "isms" have ordered as well as confused our thinking for at least a century. They were useful in grouping technical, chronological and stylistic entities and allowed for rationalizations that rendered plausible the transition from one sensibility and its pictorial analogy to another. They have been harmful as they interposed themselves between viewer and work inhibiting through the very forcefulness of the notion of the "ism", the simplicity and the clarity of the confrontation. *Neo-Impressionism* has not escaped such a double-edged heritage and a renewed seeing of the works as well as a rethinking of the underlying concepts therefore is called for periodically to check the validity of inherited ideas against the evidence of the assembled paintings and drawings.

Historically, *Neo-Impressionism* followed in the wake of the fundamental pictorial realignment that took place about a century ago when *Impressionism* came to denote a way of painting and seeing proposed by Monet, Renoir, Pissarro, and the other now famous names of that pioneering generation. The new departure from *Impressionism* preceded such early 20th century styles as *Fauvism* and *Cubism* to which it contributed essential features. Upon the freer, more spontaneous and less self-conscious Impressionist mode, *Neo-Impressionism* acted as a corrective on the assumption that a less ephemeral and more stable, calculated, and systematic approach would achieve desirable creative objectives that were beyond the scope and partly outside of the awareness of the earlier style. To be sure, Georges Seurat, the founding figure and the most forceful protagonist among the Neo-Impressionist painters would have preferred an absolute rather than a relative terminology that avoided any reference to Impressionism to denote the emerging identity of the dotted surfaces and therefore proposed *Chromo-luminarism* as an alternative. Despite the precision of this *terminus technicus* with its emphasis upon a color-light continuum, the designation never took hold while *Pointillism* which is sometimes used as a synonym refers merely to the method of paint application and therefore fails to convey as much as one might wish. For better of worse therefore *Neo-Impressionism* with its connotation of a new Impressionist sub-category remains the accepted name of a pictorial expression that came into being in the 1880s through the daring and convincing innovations of Seurat, continued by Signac and others. It passed into history around the end of the century's first decade as a shortlived but influential phase in modern art that has bequeathed formal awareness as well as theories derived from these to subsequent generations of painters.

The presentation of *Neo-Impressionism* through an historically informed, contemporary sensibility and its translation into exhibition form required a combination of rare capabilities which the Guggenheim Museum was fortunate to find in the exhibition's Curator, Professor Robert Herbert, of Yale University, who selected the exhibition and provided the documentation for the catalogue with the support of this Museum's technical staffs. We are most grateful to Dr. Herbert and through him to all those whose contributions made this occasion possible.

Thomas M. Messer, Director
The Solomon R. Guggenheim Museum

PREFACE

Mere accident and purposeful seeking each play a role in the selection of paintings and drawings for an exhibition. If we are charitable to the fallibility of human wisdom, we might liken the historian's methods to a sieve: absolutely patterned and regular, but with gaps. If all the works of art could be sifted with this tool, although imperfect, the results might be consistent. As it is, many have to be set aside reluctantly because they cannot be borrowed, and others because they cannot be located. In this exhibition, Albert Dubois-Pillet has fewer paintings than he deserves, and only the *Parade* represents Seurat's major figure compositions.

For those works actually selected, quality was the measuring device, rather than the wish to include a given type of picture or artist. Although a conscious method, it led to a number of unforeseen results. The happiest were in the form of historical lessons that flowed, without preconceptions, from this initial standard of quality, and which alerted me to aspects of Neo-Impressionism of which I was only imperfectly aware.

Over half the oils in the show are from the period 1886–1892, and the next largest concentration, about one-fifth, are from the years 1902–1909. This is a more resounding confirmation than one would have expected of the two principal periods of Neo-Impressionism, the early days when Seurat was alive, and the Fauve period when Signac and Cross were the dominant artists. The same figures expose the falling-off of Neo-Impressionism between the two periods, so much so that the word moribund is appropriate for the late 1890s.

It was less surprising to find that still life was so little favored by the Neo-Impressionists: only six are included. Figure paintings are more important, but still number only fifteen. All the rest are landscapes, views of country and city, and these are nearly always horizontal in format (the vertical, favored by the Cubists, is too dynamic for the stability the Neo-Impressionists sought). Sixteen of the landscapes have prominent figures and are perhaps of an intermediate classification, but that still leaves landscape in a position of marked dominance.

Another interesting discovery is that a generous number of paintings are included which were shown with the major exhibition societies of Paris and Brussels from 1888 to 1892. By indicating these in the Chronology as well as in the individual entries, I have tried to encourage regrouping of the paintings by exhibition year, to supplement the catalogue's grouping by artist.

All major Neo-Impressionists are represented in the exhibition, but only those less well-known artists have been included whose best pictures were obtainable. Matisse, Van Gogh and others were chosen if they passed through periods when Neo-Impressionism was important to them. Another category is formed by those like Monet or Braque whose paintings bear important relationships to Neo-Impressionism and help elucidate its life as a style.

I have thrown the weight of the catalogue towards the individual pictures and their commentaries, partly because large numbers of them are unknown, partly because unlike a book, an exhibition catalogue is a composite of individual choices and should reflect that structure. All Neo-Impressionists are given biographies, which are proportionately more complete for the least known whom the reader could not easily discover in other publications. Biographies are not provided for artists who had only brief moments as Neo-Impressionists.

Only early exhibitions are listed under each painting, since they are the ones of greatest historical significance. I have been as thorough as possible in my researches into the history of all paintings by Neo-Impressionists, and have sometimes been able to add to their records of exhibition and ownership, even in Seurat's case. The same researches have often permitted the identification of existing paintings with those in the early exhibitions, when it was thought that they were lost. Exhibitions of that era did not include dimensions and were frequently cavalier in their choice of titles. When not certain, therefore, I have used ''probably'' to indicate the largest measure of likelihood and ''perhaps'' when the evidence is favorable, but less secure. The word ''gallery'' has been omitted except when ambiguity would result, and I have not mentioned art dealers in the provenances unless they owned the pictures as private collectors.

To Dr. Jean Sutter I owe an enormous debt in the preparation of the exhibition and the catalogue. A gifted archivist, he is largely responsible for rescuing from oblivion the life and work of Louis Hayet, and he has contributed fundamentally to the biographies of Albert Dubois-Pillet, Léo Gausson, Maximilien Luce, Hippolyte Petitjean and Georges Seurat. For these and other artists he has located unpublished paintings and drawings, and he has interceded for the loans of several. He has also volunteered important documents, and has generally acted as the exhibition's best friend in Paris.

Several of the artists' heirs began by welcoming repeated visits, and ended by offering documents, photographs, and even their own time for research: Mmes. Ginette Signac, Françoise Cachin-Nora, Messrs. Pierre Angrand, Floris Bremmer, Fritz and Luke Herrmann, M. and Mme. H. Thevenin-

Lemmen, and M. and Mme. Pierre Lemmen. Marevna gave me most of the information about her work, and she and her daughter have collaborated in tracing paintings.

Among collectors who have lent to the exhibition, I owe thanks in particular to Mr. and Mrs. Arthur G. Altschul, Mr. and Mrs. W. J. Holliday, Mr. and Mrs. Hugo Perls, and Mr. and Mrs. Samuel Josefowitz. Their devotion to Neo-Impressionism has meant the establishment of important private collections and libraries which they have so kindly given me free access to. Similarly, Messrs. Oscar Ghez, Edouard Senn, Robert Lehman and his Curator Dr. Georges Szabó have been generous and forbearing in their assistance.

In Paris, Mmes. H. Adhémar and M. T. Lemoyne de Forges of the Galeries du Jeu de Paume et de l'Orangerie, and M. Bernard Dorival of the Musée National d'Art Moderne were extremely helpful. My colleague M. Pierre Rosenberg of the Louvre offered constant support, and I am grateful also to M. Michel Laclotte, Conservateur du Département des Peintures, to M. P. Quoniam, Inspecteur Général des Musées, to Mme. D. Demetz of the same office, and for information and assistance, to Messrs. J. C. Bellier, J. Fouquet, M. Kaganovitch and B. Lorenceau.

In Belgium, my work on both Belgian and French artists relied on the good offices of Mr. J. C. Parmentier, Executive Secretary of the Bureau d'Etudes et de Recherches Scientifiques, who acted as my host in Brussels, Mme. C. Lemaire of the Société Henry Van de Velde, Mmes. F. C. Legrand, P. Mertens and M. J. Chartrain-Hebbelinck of the Musées Royaux des Beaux-Arts, Messrs. J. Coquelet of the Musée d'Ixelles and R. Rousseau of the Palais des Beaux-Arts at Charleroi.

In Holland, Dr. Ellen Joosten of the Rijksmuseum Kröller-Müller facilitated the remarkably generous loan that museum has made, and answered innumerable inquiries. Dr. J. M. Joosten of the Rijksbureau voor Kunsthistorische Documentatie in The Hague and his colleagues put their fine library at my disposal and gave me much of their time.

In Helsinki, Dr. Aune Lindström, Director of the Art Gallery of Ateneum, interceded for several loans and gave much of the new information on A. W. Finch. Dr. W. Kramm, Director of the Kassel museum, supplied all the material about Paul Baum, and is responsible for the restoration and exhibition of the oeuvres of both Baum and Curt Herrmann.

In Switzerland, Professor Gert Schiff of the Swiss Institute for Art Research and New York University was my host and counselor. Dr. Hans Lüthy, Director of the Swiss Institute,

and his colleagues were also generous in their help, and
Dr. Erika Billeter of the Kunstgewerbemuseum in Zurich let
me study her manuscript catalogue of Van de Velde's
paintings.

In Milan, Mrs. Virginia Lazzati arranged many interviews and
expedited several loans. Mr. and Mrs. Riccardo Jucker,
Mr. and Mrs. Gianni Mattioli and Mr. and Mrs. Lamberto
Vitali gave me valued advice as well as the hospitality of
their collections.

For the example that their writings and teaching on Neo-
Impressionism have set, I value above all others my colleagues
George Heard Hamilton, John Rewald and Meyer Schapiro.
Conversations with Max Kozloff, especially concerning
H. E. Cross, have been a vital tonic, and Joshua Taylor gave
indispensable counsel for Italian painting and collections.

For the generous contribution of color plates, I am indebted
to Mr. and Mrs. Arthur G. Altschul, Mr. and Mrs. Lester
Avnet, Margit Chanin Ltd., M. Oscar Ghez, Hammer
Galleries, and Hirschl and Adler Galleries.

To Thomas M. Messer, Director of the Solomon R. Guggenheim Museum, I am grateful on several grounds, not the
least of which is his willingness to give me a completely free
hand in selecting the exhibition and writing the catalogue.
He, Dr. Louise Averill Svendsen, Curator, Miss Sandra Leff,
research assistant, Miss Linda Konheim, who acted as editor
of the catalogue in its final stages, and Mr. Arthur S. Congdon,
who designed it, all managed to forgive the difficulties caused
by my being outside the Museum staff, and compensated by
inventiveness as well as by excellence. In New Haven, Miss
Helen Chillman, Art Librarian of Yale University, was
particularly helpful, as was Mrs. Helen Cooper. Mrs. Patricia
Beach, Mrs. Lila Calhoun and Mrs. Jennifer Berry managed
to interweave some of the cares of this project into their
duties in the History of Art Department. My wife has given
me alert guidance in every phase of the exhibition, and was
largely responsible for the editing of the prose texts of the
catalogue.

R. L. H.
October 1967

LENDERS

NEO-IMPRESSIONISM

At an exhibition of Neo-Impressionism in 1893, a woman peered over the entrance turnstile at the paintings inside, while debating whether or not to pay the modest fee to one of the painters seated at the cash box. "Were these done by machine, Monsieur?" she asked. "No, Madame", he calmly replied, "they were done by hand".

Even today, with all the tolerance acquired by exposure to decades of machine-age art, we can still sympathize with the woman's puzzlement, as much as we can admire the artist's aplomb. Paintings covered with small dabs of almost maddening regularity are not calculated to make us feel comfortable. With their strong and contrasting colors, these dotted surfaces dance and wobble before our eyes, and refuse to settle into the mechanical uniformity which their orderly placement seems to call for. They shimmer and vibrate, and even rasp our sight like some multicolored grater.

A Neo-Impressionist painting also rubs our mind with contradictory feelings. At certain times we sense the methodical structure so strongly that we are inclined to dismiss the artist as a mere automaton, who must have filled his picture with thousands of piston-like movements of his arm, no more inspired than a man on an assembly line who repeats the same motion over and over again. At other times, the remarkable vibrations of color make us think of the artist as the opposite of the robot, as a kind of alchemist who concocts his chromatic fantasies out of the vials and philtres of scientific theory, and who surrounds himself with the mumbo-jumbo of pseudo-scientific explanations.

The artists lent themselves to both views. "I paint my method", said Seurat, "that's all there is to it". And yet, far from being products of an automatic recipe, Seurat's paintings are saturated in a unique poetry in which enigma jostles plainness and passion crowds in upon restraint.

Such apparent contradictions are the richness of art. By exploring them, we can hope to uncover some of the disparate threads of the fabric of Neo-Impressionism, in which pairs of opposites are so often intertwined. Arising from Impressionism, and foretold by it, Neo-Impressionism nonetheless wove itself into a strong current of anti-Impressionism. Devoted to the most modern subjects, and consciously seeking to express contemporary life, it paradoxically contained visible echoes of Egypt, Greece, the Quattrocento, Poussin and Claude. Seeking to produce the effects of real color-light, it created highly abstract visions. Calling upon the tradition of rational and scientific thought, it had its strongest appeal to the Fauves, those "wild beasts" of unreason and extravagance.

IMPRESSIONISM AND NEO-IMPRESSIONISM

Neo-Impressionism means simply new Impressionism, "neo" in the sense of recent, latest. The term was invented in the autumn of 1886 by the critic Félix Fénéon to describe the painting of Georges Seurat, Paul Signac, Camille and Lucien Pissarro, who had shown together at the eighth and last Impressionist exhibition in the previous May.

The most notable feature of Impressionism, its choppy brushwork and strong color, had resulted from a wish to exploit the intensity of nature seen freshly, without reflection, a kind of instant realism of vision in which the sketch became the final picture. Forms were seen indistinctly and brushstrokes were impetuous and irregular because only that way could the artist record quickly his impressions, and leave in the movements of pigment the imprint of his emotions.

Suddenly, the new Impressionists proclaimed that intense color and shimmering light need not spring from this hedonism of the retina. On the contrary, they insisted, the vibration of colored light must come from the patient and systematic application of nature's immutable laws. With Seurat's monumental *Sunday Afternoon on the Island of the Grande Jatte* as standard bearer, these artists exhibited works in bright colors laid down in tiny and systematic dabs of paint. Their paintings breathed a spirit of clear order, firm decision, scientific logic, and a startling definiteness of structure that constituted an open challenge to the instinctive art of the Impressionists of the previous decade. The most conspicuous act of defiance was their mechanical brushwork, which deliberately suppressed the personality of the artist and so flouted the individualism dear to the Impressionists.

This reaction against the Impressionists' devotion to the sensory moment grew rapidly and was remarkably widespread in the years 1886–1890. The appeal of Neo-Impressionism to painters was such that the original four were quickly joined by a number of others, some of whom had been following parallel routes: Albert Dubois-Pillet, Léo Gausson, E. G. Cavallo-Peduzzi in 1886, and Maximilien Luce, Louis Hayet, and Charles Angrand in 1887. Van Gogh himself, Toulouse-Lautrec, Emile Bernard, Emile Schuffenecker, Henri Delavallée and many others went through Neo-Impressionist phases at the same time, and in Belgium, the new style made such inroads that by 1889 it was established as the dominant movement there.

Abrupt as this anti-Impressionism was, it was nevertheless prepared by changing currents within Impressionism. By the middle 1880s, Renoir was claiming that "I had wrung Impressionism dry", and he had turned towards Ingres, Raphael and the classical tradition in his paintings of monumental nudes. Pissarro had tightened and systematized his brushwork at the beginning of the decade, and joining the young Neo-Impressionists in early 1886 was a logical step for him to take.

Another indication of the profound shift taking place in French art from 1886 onwards was the development at exactly the same time of the mature styles of Gauguin, Toulouse-Lautrec and Van Gogh. Like the Neo-Impressionists, they separated themselves from the sensual immediacy of early Impressionism. "The imagination", Van Gogh wrote in 1888, "is certainly a faculty which we must develop, one which alone can lead us to the creation of a more exalting and consoling nature than the simple brief glance at reality—which in our sight is ever changing, passing like a flash of lightning—can let us perceive."[1]

The best evidence for the attitudes underlying the Neo-Impressionists' reaction to Impressionism, aside from their paintings, is in the writing of leading Symbolists such as Félix Fénéon, Gustave Kahn, Paul Adam, Emile Verhaeren, or Jean Ajalbert. They were the intimate friends of Seurat, Signac and the other painters, meeting with them constantly and acting as their spokesmen. In their many essays on Neo-Impressionism, the one charge they most often level against Impressionism is superficiality, due to the excessive devotion to one brief moment of time. We need not accept this as true, of course, but they repeatedly accused their elders of "making nature grimace to prove that its moment is unique",[2] of providing "the confused and crude impression of an air played by a music box" instead of a properly orchestrated harmony.[3] Fénéon's favorite terms for Impressionism were "anecdote", "nomenclature", "the fugitive" and "mere objective reality", to which he opposed the virtues of Neo-Impressionism, "arabesque", "synthesis", "the permanent" and "superior reality". This generation, writers and painters both, established a prejudice that lasted until Abstract Expressionism in the 1950s, by claiming that the retinal image denied memory, associations with the past, and associations therefore with the durable and the permanent.

In Neo-Impressionism the Symbolists particularly admired the stripping away of the casual and accidental features of reality to reveal the "essence" of form, which for them was a superior truth. Much influenced by German Romantic thought, they concluded that the Impressionists were mere copyists, but that Seurat, Signac and the new painters created the reality of pure Idea. Fénéon praised the Neo-Impressionists for creating "the very sensation of life: objective reality is for them simply the theme for the creation of a superior and sublime reality in which their personality is transfused."[4]

Of course the forms whose essences were thus captured were modern forms, and one characteristic of Neo-Impressionism was its devotion to contemporary city streets, industrial suburbs and commercial riverbanks. Even in the coastal ports where most of them spent their summers, they chose the homely, ordinary architecture rather than the medieval churches or other sites which tradition had sanctioned. To these modern subjects the painters brought a technique that was patently modern. In Pissarro's terminology, it was "scientific" as against the "romantic" manner of the Impressionists.[5]

For all this wilful modernity, the arbitrary and simplified forms of Neo-Impressionism—the "essences" of the Symbolists—were the very embodiment of contact with the past, with the spirit of continuity and permanence which they sought in opposition to the fleeting moment of present time celebrated by the Impressionists. Paul Adam, writing in the *Revue Contemporaine* in May 1886, typifies the Symbolist view, in which scientific modernism is linked with "primitive" styles of the past:

■ It no longer suffices to reproduce a concept with settings which provide us with the superfluous memory of associative sensations. It is necessary to abstract from them the influence of lessons transmitted atavistically, and to pursue the subjectivity of apperception to its most abstract formula.

As much by the intransigent application of scientific coloring as by the strange qualities of innovators, Messrs. Camille Pissarro, Signac and Seurat mark today most manifestly the definitive tendency of impressionist art.

The varied and melodious forms of the primitives suits the new generation. Extraordinary analogies present themselves between the composition of ancient frescoes and those of certain impressionists.

[In *A Sunday Afternoon on the Island of the Grande Jatte*]: Even the stiffness of the people, the ready-made forms helps give the sound of modernity, the recall of our tight clothing, glued to the body, the reserved gestures, the British manner everywhere imitated. We

■ assume attitudes like those of Memling's personages. M. Seurat has perfectly seen, understood, conceived and translated this with the pure composition of the primitives.

In summary, this exhibition [i.e., the last Impressionist show] initiates a new art, eminently remarkable by the scientific bases of its processes, by the return to primitive forms, and by the philosophical concern for rendering pure apperception.

The "primitive" and "ancient" styles which the Symbolists most frequently named in connection with the Neo-Impressionists were the Egyptian, Greek, Gothic and early Renaissance. By the 1880s, these represented the healthy and vigorous residue of the old classical tradition, and were found in Puvis de Chavannes and Gauguin as well as in Seurat. What is remarkable is that styles and ideas associated in the 1860s and 1870s with extreme conservatism, became the instruments of revolution in the 1880s.

A student in traditional schools from 1875–1879, Seurat had absorbed a love of Egyptian and antique art, of early Renaissance art and Ingres. When subsequently he adopted the Impressionists' color-light and naturalistic subject matter, he instinctively reformed their style according to the classical preference for idealized and clearly stated forms. The closeness of this tradition to the Symbolists' outlook is what made Seurat their chosen artist. Their esthetic owed a great debt to the same conservative critic Charles Blanc, whom Seurat had read and annotated when a boy. How much like the Symbolists is the sound of Blanc's *Grammar of the Arts of Design:*

■ The artist is charged with the task of recalling to us the ideal, that is, of revealing to us the primitive beauty of things, of discovering the imperishable character, the pure essence. The ideas which nature manifests in a confused form [as in Impressionism!], art defines and illuminates.

Along comes the artist: he stops the sun, he suspends the course of human time, and he removes from this beauty the unessential part, time, in order to make it appear in the eternity of life.[6]

Not just for the Symbolists, but for all subsequent artists, Seurat and the Neo-Impressionists made available the whole vast reservoir of traditional ideas and forms associated with the past. They did this by bending them to new purposes,

and by giving them an acceptably modern guise which had such an appeal to the new industrial society: scientific color theory.

COLOR AND COLOR THEORY

It is not at all clear to what extent the older Impressionists might have been concerned with color theory. All artists are conscious of color, and the Impressionists were the first generation to grow up with the new chemical pigments that came supplied in tubes, but there is no evidence that they were as interested in theory as was, say, Delacroix. It is true that by the middle 1870s, critics who defended them claimed that they decomposed colored light into its constituent tones in a scientific manner, and thus that their art represented a superior kind of objective truth. More than anything else, however, these claims were calculated to offer the comfort of a rational explanation to a public shocked by the apparent unreality of the new art. They also succeeded in establishing an aura of scientific discussion upon which the Neo-Impressionists could easily build, just as the actual practice of the Impressionists, whether shored up by theory or not, provided varied examples which could be codified.

Neo-Impressionist color theory had its origins in 1881, when Seurat made extensive notes on Delacroix' paintings, copied out some of his remarks on color, and read the new French translation of Ogden Rood's *Modern Chromatics*. Rood offered the best summary of the latest theories of color, including those of scientists and of critics like Ruskin. He gave an especially lucid explanation, based upon Helmholtz, of the differences between color as pure light, and color as painters' pigment. It was the failure to realize these differences that had led the chemist Michel Chevreul, Delacroix, and many critics of Impressionism into contra-dictory findings. By 1886, the Neo-Impressionists, with Rood's substantial help, could claim an apparently integral color theory, which was duly expounded by Fénéon and other friendly critics.

Pigments, first of all, must be recognized as lacking the power and the purity of real colored light rays, and the laws deduced from the study of light cannot be transferred directly to pigments. For example, color-opposites in light rays, such as greenish-yellow and violet, will produce white when the rays intersect, but two pigments so colored will form a dull brownish-grey. The reasons are many, but principally that the light source in the second case would be the natural or artificial light that happened to illuminate the painted surface, and not the separate and pure color-components of light. Furthermore, when this light strikes the mixed pigments, the solid impurities fortify one another and absorb irregularly much of the color. Even violet paint by itself, being solid matter, reflects portions of other colors than its own, although we allow ourselves to be dominated by the one hue. These other colors, when mixed with the similar "other colors" of the greenish-yellow, combine to form the dull result.

The conclusion drawn by the Neo-Impressionists was that the pigments must be broken down to different hues to avoid the palette mixtures that lead to inert tones. The Impressionists had already divided their colors, but into relatively few tones which were customarily close together, such as yellow, yellow-green and bluish-green. These tones were only partly separated, because the Impressionists placed one wet stroke atop another, and portions of them were mixed together. The result was the scumbled and greyed effects which are often the source of their paintings' unity, but which the Neo-Impressionists found dull.

The essence of Impressionist color was harmony based on similar and related hues; the essence of Neo-Impressionist color was harmony based on contrasting hues.

In a typical Neo-Impressionist painting, a meadow struck by full sunlight will have these separate colors: several different greens, representing the local color of grass which absorbs most of the colors except itself; orange, orange-yellow and yellow, representing elements of pure sunlight and only slightly altered sunlight reflected from the grassy surfaces; greenish-yellow, representing partly absorbed sunlight and simultaneously the color-opposite of the neighboring violet in the shaded portion of the field. In shadow, the field will have stronger greens since the local color is not overpowered by sunlight; blues will represent the quality of indirect light and, more importantly, the color-opposite of the orange-yellow in the sunlit areas; reddish-purples represent the opposite of the sunlit greens; some sparse oranges show the presence of particles of pure sunlight that penetrate the shade. In addition to all these, smaller quantities of yet other colors can occur if neighboring areas are in a position to reflect some of their own hues. Typically also, the contrasts will be fortified at the edge where the sunlit and shaded areas meet, the light colors being still lighter and more intense, the darker ones, darker and also more intense. The result is the pulsating bands of haloes and umbrae that are especially characteristic of Neo-Impressionism.

It becomes clear that a great many pigments are used, *and*

not just the three primaries, nor even just the six principal colors. At its extreme reduction in the 1880s (in Seurat's late paintings), the Neo-Impressionist range consisted of eighteen mixtures on the palette before application to the canvas, and each of the eighteen could be mixed with white in any degree. The myth of the three primaries, which persists despite the marvelous debunking by J. Carson Webster, is a case of bewildered critics trying to comfort their readers with an apparent explanation. Actually, the "primaries" are not the same for light as for pigments. Yellow and blue light rays form white, but yellow and blue pigments make green.

It is perhaps equally clear that contrasts of color are a distinguishing feature of Neo-Impressionism. Ordinarily these are not opposing colors intermixed in one and the same area. A greenish-yellow field does not demand that violet strokes be placed there, but instead in the shaded area next to it. *Color opposites are placed in juxtaposed areas, to exalt one another by contrast.* This is the principle followed by Gauguin and the Nabis, and one of the reasons why they were interested in much the same color theory. To return to our original example of the grassy meadow, the sunlit area has largely allied hues—greens and yellows—with the oranges providing the nearest approach to opposition. Reds and violets, the true opposites, do not appear there but in the shaded portion of the field next to it. The will toward contrast was so strong in Neo-Impressionism that everything conspired toward the fortification of the juxtaposed contrasts, including the haloes at the meeting edges, the frequent opposition of light and dark, the crisp geometry of the forms, and their common orientation at right angles to one another.

TECHNIQUE AND SCIENCE

At the heart of Neo-Impressionist theory lies *mélange optique*, the optical mixture in the observer's eye of the separate particles of color. According to the painters and their friendly critics, the impurities and dull tones of traditional palette mixtures could be overcome by rendering the several constituent colors in separate strokes. These different colors would then combine in our eye to reconstitute the dominant hue sought after.

That this does not happen in Neo-Impressionist paintings is a shock to the innocent observer. He discovers that with rare exceptions, he continues to see the separate colors no matter what his distance. Why then was the theory proclaimed?

First, because it was a defense of the separate colors the artists really wanted and it therefore offered the support of a rational explanation. Observers could overcome the discomfort of the unknown and set about looking at the pictures with the conviction that they were party to the secret. Second, although it does not happen, it is *toward* this optical mixture that the eye struggles. In so doing, an active vibration takes place in which the separate colors are seen in a stimulating shimmer. It is this vibration which forces the viewer to be active and which recapitulates the intensity of real light dancing and sparkling over varied natural surfaces.

Vibration was the word which Seurat found in Charles Blanc's description of Delacroix' color mixtures,[7] and it remains the best description of the effects in his own painting. Instead of using yellow and blue to form green, as the misguided critics sometimes said, Seurat used several different greens for a grassy area, much as did Delacroix and the Impressionists. The essential vibration was that of the local color. Then he added, as has been seen, a number of other colors in varying quantities. Our eye registers the dominant green, but also these other hues without "mixing" them to form one uniform color. And Signac, when he wrote his defence of optical mixing in his book in 1899, was using brushstrokes as large as the tiles of mosaic, which neither he nor anyone looking at his paintings, would really have thought capable of "mixing".

A moment's reflection shows not only that real optical fusion was not the artists' goal, but also that it is impossible to achieve. Each particle of pigment reflects light, it is not itself a light source, and hence it will not act like a ray of pure light. The eye, besides, is not like a prism and cannot duplicate the recombining of whole light that has been broken into its constituents—even were this possible in pigments. Still other objections can be raised to show the impossibility of duplicating optical color in a picture: A red dress in reality will be life-size, but it might be only a few inches large in a painting, and absolute area is a determining factor in the effect produced by a color. The same red dress in nature might be seen against the receding angle of grass and trees, but in a painting the "background" is actually the flat plane next to, not behind the red dress, and all color relationships will be different.

The most elemental question of all has been raised by Meyer Schapiro on several occasions: How can one literally be "scientific" in painting? The Neo-Impressionist painter seized upon certain ephemeral reactions in nature and exploited them. The physicists they studied had described these reactions, but in order to warn the artist against them, precisely because they were transient effects. Which adopts the more "scientific" attitude, the physicist who edits away a given color event, or the painter who exposes it?

The degree to which Neo-Impressionist technique can be called "scientific" lies in the realm of metaphor and style. It was their wish to appear as technicians of art, and it was their instinct to stamp every aspect of their painting and theory with the mark of contemporary science.[8] It is for this reason that those aspects must be examined, for to dismiss them because they are not "true" science would be to overlook the salient quality of Neo-Impressionism. In art, what is true is not scientific fact, but whatever contributes to the formation of the object.

So strong was the spirit of the rational technician among the Neo-Impressionists that the omnipresent dotted brushstroke seems the only proper vehicle for it. If they merely wanted small dabs of paint, they could have made them in all shapes and placed them irregularly. Nothing in color theory requires the systematic apportionment of the small strokes. It was not a scientific act, but an expression of the artist's role as inventor, weaving his color fabric methodically thanks to his control of the mysteries of natural law. "A conscious and scientific manner" Fénéon called their technique, "an impersonal and as it were abstract treatment", which he contrasted to the "accidents", the "arbitrariness", or the "improvisation" of the Impressionists. And in 1887, converted to the new style, Pissarro called himself one of the "scientific Impressionists" who could no longer look comfortably upon the work of the "romantic Impressionists". Monet's brush-work offended him "by the disorder which stands out in this romantic fantasy which, despite the artist's talent, is not in accord with our epoch", and he once went so far as to call Monet's brushwork "rancid".[9]

There were other reasons which rooted the uniform brush-work of the Neo-Impressionists deeply in their practice. To avoid the improvisations and the uneven results of Impressionism, they put small strokes atop others already dry. In this way, the pigments did not mix chemically and alter their color, and they also dried evenly. The thick strokes of the Impressionists often were still molten in the interior after the outer surfaces had dried, setting up a tension which led to cracking. Another advantage was that the regular dabs did not cast little shadows nor reflect light irregularly (the "disorder" Pissarro saw in Impressionism), and they could readily conform to the precise contours of the forms, instead of producing the ragged edges of Impressionism. The small strokes are not as regular as they seem from a distance or in the small scale of reproduction, but their relative evenness and small size permitted an almost infinite nuance of color and the accumulation in a small area of myriad tones which larger and scumbled strokes would not.

Despite the impression it gives, the technique of the Neo-Impressionists did not necessarily require more time than most others. It is the systematic appearance of the dots which makes us think so. Meyer Schapiro has commented that the many layers of glazes in a Venetian painting would demand as much time, and it is a demonstrable fact that the Neo-Impressionists were prolific painters. In the last seven years of his short life, Seurat produced six monumental canvases, thirty-four of average size, seventy small panels (and over one-hundred of his mature drawings). Technique anyway is the servant of the master. Mondrian, with his ostensibly simple manner, finished only a handful of paintings a year. "Technique", said Pissarro, "we regard as nothing". Originality for an artist "consists in the character of his composition and the vision particular to each artist".[10]

Also expressive of what can be called the scientific attitude of the Neo-Impressionists were the various devices and materials they employed. They spurned varnish, for example, and instead put their paintings under glass, to avoid the discoloration and refraction caused by the traditional coating. Seurat painted his famous *Models* [Barnes Foundation] on gesso—doubtless a thin coating of plaster applied in a liquid state—and Hayet worked with an encaustic mixture instead of oil. Most of them made special frames, some white, some tinted, and some multicolored. Following Seurat's example, Finch, Lemmen and Van Rysselberghe painted narrow borders of contrasting colors directly on their canvases. By themselves, such inventions might not distinguish the Neo-Impressionists from other artists who paid attention to the framing and protection of their canvases, but taken together with their rigorous technique, they were signals to contemporaries that they were in the hands of craftsmen determined to renew every element of their trade. The colored borders and frames in particular must have struck contemporaries with the force that some of the recent innovations of "Op Art" have had on us.

THE ABSTRACT COMPONENTS OF ART

From ancient times, colors and lines have been associated with human emotions. Red has usually indicated the strong feelings of passion or danger, and blue the sense of calmness and peace. Similarly, agitated lines moving upward will automatically induce a feeling of excitement, and horizontal lines, of serenity. Like so many other elements of tradition, the Neo-Impressionists worked these associations into their theories, and here, too, they consulted contemporary science.

In 1886, during the last Impressionist exhibition, Seurat, Signac and the Pissarros met the brilliant young mathematician and esthetician, Charles Henry (1859–1926). Henry was an intimate friend of the Symbolist writers Félix Fénéon and Gustave Kahn, and doubtless it was through them that the painters came to know him. Mathematician, inventor, physiologist, Henry was also a man of letters and collaborated with Fénéon, Kahn, and others on the new Symbolist reviews.[11] His writings on color were especially influential, and both painters and writers attended the lecture-demonstrations he held regularly in his apartment. Signac went so far as to provide diagrams and plates for Henry's lectures and books, from 1888 through 1890.

Henry's writings on color incorporated all the latest theories and were even more up-to-date than Rood's book of 1881, so it was only natural that the Neo-Impressionists would be drawn to him. What especially attracted them was his discussion of the way colors affect an observer. Whereas Charles Blanc, whom Seurat had studied earlier, limited himself to stating the traditional associations, Henry carried them further and added physiological explanations. He brought the rather vague theory of emotional associations into the realm of science and this, given the Neo-Impressionists' orientation, was a necessary prelude to their enthusiasm. Henry did not stop there, however, and took also the final step of bringing associational theory from the world of science into that of artistic sensation. In this case, the linking of color to linear direction and to placement in painting was his most original contribution.

Charles Blanc's *Grammar of the Arts of Design* had already brought the theory of linear expression to the attention of the artists. Referring to the work of Humbert de Superville at the beginning of the century, Blanc had stressed the relationships between horizontal lines and the expression of calm monumentality, or vertical lines and sensuous gaiety.

Once again Henry took these theories into the sphere of contemporary science. His first major statement was *A Scientific Esthetic*, a brochure published in 1885. About a year later, on a drawing for his *Parade*, Seurat recorded the principal words (here italicized) from this passage in the book:

■ The problem of an esthetic of forms comes down to this: What are *the most agreeable lines*? But a little

■ reflection shows us quickly that the line is an *abstraction*: it is the synthesis of the two parallel and opposite *directions* in which it can be inscribed; the reality is the direction. I do not see a circle: I only see circles inscribed in one direction or in another, which one calls "cycles". The problem leads to the conclusion announced: What are the agreeable directions? What are the disagreeable directions? In other words, what directions do we associate with *pleasure* and with *pain*?

Henry meant that certain lines, such as those moving upward and to the right, are natural to the human and therefore agreeably associated with his unconscious mental movements as he looks at them; angles opening out to the right or circles swirling to the right, the way our hand moves when using a pencil sharpener, are equally natural, hence agreeable. On the other hand, lines and angles moving "backward", that is, down and to the left, are disagreeable, and the artist can exploit this unconscious feeling if he wishes. Because a line is not static, but recalls the moving point that made it, the directions of the lines of a painting become all important.

Following the German scientist Fechner, Henry charted all directions and relationships according to their physiological reactions. Then he wedded to them a similar distribution of colors according to their own emotional associations, and provided artists with easily used lists and diagrams which correlated all features of his grand synthesis.

Henry's theories of color and linear composition were integrated into Neo-Impressionism by the late 1880s, and helped form a remarkably homogeneous whole. Seurat's *Parade* is probably the best example of the way the scientist's work fitted into the complexity of artistic style. The little drawing for the picture, which cites Henry's words, also reproduces the diagram defining the Golden Section, one of the geometric harmonies Henry had found most satisfying to observers of paintings. Seurat actually built his painting on the Golden Section (the proportion in which the smaller of two parts is to the larger, as the larger is to the sum of both), and he correlated the horizontal and downward-sloping lines with a balance of gay and sad colors to produce the picture's lambent melancholy. Its aura of permanence and monumentality owes much to the strict composition, which has the elegant clarity of an engineer's straight edge and compass.

The artists would not have accepted Henry's theories so readily if they had not already been part of the mood generated by Symbolism, in which they all shared. The Symbolists openly proclaimed the necessary union of poetry, painting and music because of their least common denominator: the emotions they could arouse without regard to the images they might evoke. Téodor de Wyzéwa wrote in the *Revue Wagnérienne* in May 1886:

■ Colors and lines, [. . .] like words, have for our soul an emotional value independent of the very objects they represent [. . .]. Henceforth these colors, these contours, these expressions are tied in our souls to these emotions, and thus they have become not just signs of visual sensations, but also signs of our emotions, [. . .] like syllables of poetry, like notes of music, *emotional signs*. Thus certain painters have used colors and lines in a pure symphonic arrangement, heedless of a visual object to be painted directly.

Henry and Seurat did not use Wyzéwa's phrase "emotional signs", but they would have accepted it willingly. Poet, painter and scientist were all agreed that the basic components of art could be dealt with as autonomous elements, freed of their role as definers of natural images. "M. Seurat", wrote Fénéon in 1889, "knows well that a line, independently of its topographical role, possesses an assessable abstract value".[12] It was not just line, but the painters' concentration upon the particle of color, its relationship as pure color with another stroke of pigment, and the relationship of both color and line directly with the observer's emotion, which tended to diminish the role of natural imagery in their concepts.

Contemporaries recognized the impulsion toward abstraction as a leading quality of Neo-Impressionism. Lukewarm friends like Georges Lecomte feared that the painters "might reach the point of annuling [. . .] the reality of appearances and of character",[13] but their close friends praised them for it. Neo-Impressionism, Paul Adam said, "wants to reproduce the pure phenomenon, the subjective appearance of things. It is a school of abstraction".[14]

By "abstract", writers and painters of the period did not mean "devoid of reference to the real world", as we now use the term. They meant to draw away from nature, in the sense of disdaining imitation in order to concentrate upon the distillation of essential shapes and movements. These distilled forms were superior to nature because they partook of *idea*, and represented the dominance of the artist over the mere stuff of nature. In embryo, the Symbolists and Neo-Impressionists did establish the philosophical defence of pure abstraction, but nature still formed part of the basic dialogue. A careless emphasis on their abstraction could lead one to conclude that the artists might as well have chosen any

subjects, since nature was so seldom mentioned. Even a cursory glance at their paintings, however, shows that they had a pronounced preference for certain kinds of landscape and figure compositions. In them we feel strongly still the nineteenth century's love of nature dressed in the finery of her colored air and light.

NEO-IMPRESSIONISM IN THE TWENTIETH CENTURY

From 1886 to about 1894, Neo-Impressionism had its first life. It then fell into considerable eclipse for a decade before it re-emerged in the Fauve period. The reasons for this are not clear, but the symptoms are: Seurat and Dubois-Pillet died in 1890 and 1891. Camille Pissarro returned to his earlier style, and his son Lucien moved to England. Van de Velde and Finch gave up painting in the enthusiasm for the applied arts which swept across Europe in the early 1890s. Angrand forsook painting for drawing, and retired to Normandy. Cross, Luce, Signac and Van Rysselberghe simply produced fewer good pictures. Younger artists, meanwhile, turned toward Van Gogh, Gauguin and the Nabis group, who supplanted the Neo-Impressionists in the affections of the Symbolists.

One of the symptoms might help explain the temporary enervation of Neo-Impressionism. It is found in the letters of Signac, Cross and Angrand from about 1895 to 1905, and constituted a veritable dilemma for them. On the one hand, they liked to work with pure color harmonies, without worrying about natural color and images. On the other, they could not relinquish their instinctive love of natural phenomena. "How numerous are the attachments", Cross wrote, "that detain us among the nauseous things of our false upbringing". He dreamed of "pure chromatic compositions" composed "out of whole cloth in the studio", in which the color relationships would be self-determining, but "the reef one strikes is that the harmonious given of nature contains more surprises, more variety than the assortment of colored materials" around him in the studio.[15]

By about 1904, the resolution of the dilemma was made in favor of the abstract side of the equation. "Harmony means sacrifice", Cross said, and much of early Neo-Impressionism was jettisoned. Although they paid lip service to their established theory, Signac and Cross now painted in enormous strokes which could never pretend to mix in the eye, and which did not even retain nuance of tone. Raw, bold yellows, magentas, reds, blues and greens sprang forth from their canvases, making them as free of the trammels of nature as any painting then being done in Europe.

23

Artists began to rediscover Neo-Impressionism in the colored mosaics of Cross and Signac, and they also acquired a new interest in Signac's book of 1899, *Du Delacroix au Néo-Impressionnisme*. Following his and Cross's lead, they overlooked those aspects of Neo-Impressionism which clung to naturalism, and concentrated upon pure color theory, and upon color as the vehicle of emotional expression. In a number of essays as well as in paintings, artists like Matisse, Metzinger, Derain, Delaunay, Severini, Kupka and Kandinsky helped give Neo-Impressionist theory its second, much altered life in the years before the first World War.[16]

This second flowering of Neo-Impressionism lasted from about 1904 to 1910. Matisse and Derain, two of the principal Fauves, went through important periods as Neo-Impressionists, and most of the other Fauves flirted with it. A whole sub-style developed in the work of Delaunay and Metzinger, and it had great significance shortly afterward for their work of the Cubist period. Parallel developments took place outside Paris. In Holland, Mondrian took over from Toorop a similar mosaic divisionism in 1909 and 1910, and in Italy, the young Futurists adapted it to their dynamic art, thanks especially to Severini's work in Paris from 1907 onward.

In the period of Cubism and Futurism, 1911–1914, Seurat once again became influential. He had been neglected in previous years because the strongly colored work of Cross and Signac was more to the liking of the Fauves. With the advent of monochromatic Cubism in 1910–1911, questions of form displaced color in the artists' attention, and for these Seurat was more relevant. Thanks to several exhibitions, his paintings and drawings were easily seen in Paris, and reproductions of his major compositions circulated widely among the Cubists. The *Chahut* [Rijksmuseum Kröller-Müller, Otterlo] was called by André Salmon "one of the great icons of the new devotion",[17] and both it and the *Circus* [Louvre], according to Apollinaire, "almost belong to Synthetic Cubism".[18]

Seurat's appeal to the Cubists was not the same as Cézanne's. Cézanne's passionate dialectic with nature had been of greatest importance in the years 1908–1911, in Cubism's early and highly expressionistic phase. When the painters shifted ground toward flatter and more linear structures in 1911, they began to admire the way that Seurat "dominated his sensitivity" in front of his canvases, the way in which he asserted an absolute "scientific clarity of conception" (to cite Apollinaire).[19] In his geometric distillations of form and movement, they found that assertion of the primacy of idea over nature which the Symbolists had glorified, and they believed that he had taken a fundamental step toward Cubism by restoring intellect and order to art, after Impressionism had denied them.

Sensitive especially to Seurat's late paintings and drawings of café-concerts and circuses, subjects they were fond of, the Cubists discovered the mathematical harmonies that underlay them. The "Section d'Or" group they founded was an homage to Seurat, and another clue to their links with his generation is the fact that Delaunay, Gleizes and Severini all knew Charles Henry personally.

Seurat's rise to prominence did not completely obscure other aspects of Neo-Impressionism. Artists of the years 1910–1914, including Mondrian and Kandinsky as well as the Cubists, took support from one of its central principles: that line and color have the ability to communicate certain emotions to the observer, independently of natural form. Neo-Impressionist color theory had an important heir in the person of Robert Delaunay. He had been a Neo-Impressionist in the Fauve period, and knew intimately the writings of Signac and Henry. His famous solar discs of 1912 and 1913 are descended from the Neo-Impressionists' concentration upon the decomposition of spectral light.

After the first World War, the pulsations of Neo-Impressionism were more refined, and harder to identify. Ozenfant's and Jeanneret's doctrine of Purism paid particular homage to Seurat partly because, as Alfred Barr has suggested, his reformist spirit was a natural comfort to men engaged in reforming Cubism. Just as logically, Charles Henry cropped up again, commissioned by Ozenfant and Jeanneret to write articles in their L'Esprit Nouveau. In their teachings and writings, Gleizes, Lhote and Severini introduced Neo-Impressionist theories as a matter of course, and a generation of art students in Europe and America grew up with school lessons in the division of color. More meaningful, perhaps, was the assimilation of the spirit of Seurat and Neo-Impressionism in the art of Gris, Léger and artists attached to the De Stijl and Bauhaus movements.

The most enduring appeal of Neo-Impressionism—it reappears in Op Art of the 1960s, and perhaps also in Roy Lichtenstein's dotted surfaces—must lie in the degree to which it expresses the instincts of a society given over to science and technology. Secular and anti-mystical, the Neo-Impressionists proposed in their art the same triumph of man's rational, ordering mind that science took as its goal. Everything worked toward the same expression in their art, which is fundamentally optimistic: the declamatory framework of their compositions, the absolute control of their geometric rhythms, the precision of their contours, the technician's impersonality of their

brushwork, and even the language in which their theories were embedded.

Looking back upon the 1880s in his older years, Maurice Denis contrasted the Neo-Impressionists with his own group, the Nabis, and was still able to feel the unique excitement they generated. The Neo-Impressionists, he said,

■ only conceived of the model as luminous, of the landscape as sunstruck, and of the setting of modern life as bathed in reason and clarity. And, instead of looking back as we did, Sérusier, Bernard and myself, then close to Gauguin and Cézanne, back towards the past, towards a tradition determined by so many masterpieces, instead of frequenting the Louvre, where Bonnard, Roussel, Vallatton and Vuillard formed themselves,—they, the Neo-Impressionists, believed they were founding an entirely new art. They inaugurated a vision, a technique, an esthetic based on the recent discoveries of physics, on a scientific conception of the world and of life.[20]

It is doubtless here that we are closest to the original meaning of Neo-Impressionism and if, in our more romantic moods, we are inclined to complain that it does not have the painterly qualities of Monet or Van Gogh, we might recall the words of Amadée Ozenfant which characterize the whole group as well as Seurat: "Do not reproach Seurat for being on the line to Athens rather than on the one to Flanders; the train to Greece is a good train, are you going to blame it for not taking you to Amsterdam? One uses it when one has need, that's all, and it is advisable not to go to the wrong station."[21]

FOOTNOTES

1   Letter to Emile Bernard, April 1888, in *The Complete Letters of Vincent Van Gogh*, Greenwich, 1959, vol. 3, p. 478.

2   Félix Fénéon, "Définition du Néo-Impressionnisme", *L'Art Moderne*, vol. 7, 1 May 1887, [BIBLIOGRAPHY 5] pp. 90–95.

3   Paul Adam, "Les Impressionnistes à l'Exposition des Indépendants", *La Vie Moderne*, vol. 10, no. 15, 15 April 1888, p. 229.

4   "Définition du Néo-Impressionnisme", *op. cit.* This, and other relevant aspects of Symbolism are best summarized by A. Lehmann in *The Symbolist Aesthetic in France 1885–1895*, Oxford, 1950, and discussed in their relation to painting of the period by Sven Loevgren, *The Genesis of Modernism*, Stockholm, 1959.

5   An invaluable source for Neo-Impressionism is Pissarro's *Lettres à son fils Lucien* (John Rewald, ed.), Paris, 1950.

6   Edition of 1880 [originally published 1867], p. 14.

7   Seurat stated that he had read Blanc's "Eugène Delacroix", *Gazette des Beaux-Arts*, vol. 16, 1864, pp. 5–27, 97–129.

8   Brilliantly discussed by Meyer Schapiro, "New Light on Seurat", *Art News*, vol. 57, April 1958, pp. 22ff.

9   Letters of 7 and 9 January 1887, in *Lettres à son fils Lucien, op. cit.*, pp. 123, 124.

10 Letter of 6 November 1886 to Durand-Ruel, in Lionello Venturi (ed.), *Les Archives de l'Impressionnisme*, Paris, 1939, vol. 2, p. 24.

11 On Henry's relationships with painters and writers, see the special issue devoted to him of *Cahiers de l'Etoile*, January–February 1930, with articles by Valéry, Kahn, Signac, Gleizes and others.

12 "Exposition des Artistes Indépendants à Paris", *L'Art Moderne*, vol. 9, 27 October 1889, p. 339.

13 "L'Art Contemporain", *La Revue Indépendante*, vol. 23, April 1892, p. 13.

14 "Peintres Impressionnistes", *La Revue Contemporaine*, April–May 1886, p. 542.

15 Letters to Angrand of 23 February 1903 [BIBLIOGRAPHY 20], and to Signac of about 1898 [BIBLIOGRAPHY 23].

16 Some aspects of this are discussed by Alfred H. Barr, Jr., *Matisse, his Art and his Public*, Museum of Modern Art, 1951; Herschel B. Chipp, "Orphism and Color Theory", *Art Bulletin*, vol. 40, no. 1, March 1958, pp. 55–63; Fanette Roche, "Severini et l'Héritage Néo-Impressionniste", *L'Information d'Histoire de l'Art*, no. 1, January–February 1967, pp. 15–23.

17 *Propos d'Atelier*, Paris, 1922, p. 42.

18 *Cubist Painters, Aesthetic Meditations* [originally 1913; trans. Lionel Abel], New York, 1944, p. 22.

19 *Ibid.*, p. 22.

20 Introduction to the exhibition *Théo Van Rysselberghe*, Giroux Gallery, Brussels, 1927, p. 7.

21 "Seurat", *Cahiers d'Art*, vol. 1, no. 7, September 1926, p. 172.

NEO-IMPRESSIONISTS IN FRANCE

Charles Angrand

(1854–1926)

Angrand's art bears long meditation, but his life is quickly told. He first studied for the teaching profession, and then enrolled in the municipal art school at Rouen where, by 1880, he became known as an *enfant terrible*. His *Saint-Sever Railroad Station* (subsequently lost) exhibited that year, provoked a great controversy for its intense, luminous coloration and its naturalistic subject. He moved to Paris in 1882, and took a post teaching mathematics at the Collège Chaptal, merely to earn his living. He was a founding member of the Société des Artistes Indépendants in 1884, and came to know his fellow members Seurat, Signac and the others. Like them, he formed many close friendships with the young Symbolist writers, especially Félix Fénéon, Gustave Kahn and Emile Verhaeren, and he was admired by Van Gogh who met him in 1887. In that same year he completed his evolution toward Neo-Impressionism and was thenceforth properly regarded in contemporary reviews as a leading member of the group. He showed every year with the Indépendants and in occasional gallery exhibitions, and in 1891 was invited to exhibit with Les XX in Brussels. In that year, however, he began to show drawings in preference to paintings and, except for brief periods between 1901 and 1908, he gave up oils for conté crayon drawings and pastels. He retired to Saint-Laurent-en-Caux in 1896 and lived thereafter virtually as a recluse. In 1913 he spent a year in Dieppe, then on the eve of the war moved to Rouen, where he remained until his death. Although the last thirty years of his life were spent in isolation, he was an excellent correspondent and the most provocative theoretician among the Neo-Impressionists in that period. His large pastels of 1910 to 1925 are not as well known as his conté crayon drawings of the 1890s, but they are his finest work.

Angrand has been included in all exhibitions devoted to Neo-Impressionism; he exhibited often in Rouen from 1880 onward, and regularly with the Indépendants in Paris from 1884 until his death; the Galerie Druet included his drawings in many exhibitions from 1903 through 1913, and Bernheim-Jeune through the first three decades of this century. He was given modest one-man shows by Durand-Ruel in 1899, by the Galerie Dru in 1925, the Indépendants in 1926, the Galerie Legrip (Rouen), in 1927, Jacques Rodriguès-Henriquès in 1929, and by André Maurice in December 1960 – January 1961.

Among major works not in the present exhibition are *Inside the Rouen Museum*, 1880 (oil, Pierre Angrand, Paris); *Farmyard Scene*, 1884 (oil, Ny Carlsberg Glyptotek, Copenhagen); *Woman Sewing*, 1885 (oil, Pierre Angrand); *The Artist's Mother Sewing*, 1885 (oil, Oscar Ghez, Geneva); *Railroad Embankment, La Ligne de l'Ouest à sa sortie de Paris*, 1886 (oil, Private collection, Paris); *The Seine at Courbevoie*, 1888 (oil, formerly W. Weinberg); *The Shepherd's Star*, 1894 (crayon, Pierre Angrand); *Mother and Child*, 1898 (crayon, Oscar Ghez); *Path amongst the Apple Trees*, c. 1905 (oil, Pierre Angrand); *The Apple Harvest*, c. 1920 (pastel, Pierre Angrand).

Bibliography: See BIBLIOGRAPHY 1, 9, 20, 23, 24, 26, 27, 28 and Pierre Angrand, "Charles Angrand" in BIBLIOGRAPHY 2; Gustave Coquiot, *Georges Seurat*, Paris, 1924; "Delattre", untitled article, *Nouvelliste de Rouen*, 24 January 1888 [Angrand archives]; Félix Fénéon, "Catalogue des 33", *La Cravache*, 19 January 1889, in *Oeuvres* (J. Paulhan, ed.), Paris, 1948, pp. 156–160 and "Charles Angrand", *Bulletin de la vie artistique*, vol. 7, 15 April 1926, pp. 117–118; J. Le Fustec, "Les Palettes, Ch. Angrand", *Journal des Artistes*, vol. 6, no. 18, 8 May 1887, pp. 139–140; Gustave Kahn, "Chronique de la Littérature et de l'Art, L'Exposition des 33", *La Revue Indépendante*, vol. 6, January 1888, pp. 146–151; G. Noyer, "La Chronique Artistique", *Chronique de Rouen*, 11 August 1881 [Angrand archives].

"Angrand list" in the individual picture entries refers to the manuscript catalogue being prepared by Pierre Angrand.

1

THE SEINE AT SAINT-OUEN (LA SEINE, LE MATIN, SAINT-OUEN). 1886.
Oil on canvas, 18 × 21 1/2" (46 × 55 cm.).
Signed and dated l.l. "Ch. Angrand —86".

Early exhibitions: Paris, Indépendants, 21 August —
21 September 1886, no. 18; Paris, Georges Petit, "Exposition
des 33", December 1887 — January 1888

Collection Mr. and Mrs. Samuel Josefowitz, Switzerland.

In 1880–1882 Angrand's forthright style, despite the
controversy it provoked in Rouen, was a relatively conservative
naturalism compared with Impressionism. By 1884–1885, he
developed an original and expressive style (*Farmyard Scene*,
The Artist's Mother Sewing) in which strong color was laid
down with vigorous short strokes that were arbitrarily
parallel to one another in any given area. The hues were
opaque and rather subdued, compared to Seurat and Signac
of the same time, but Angrand's manner was an important
adumbration of the divided color-texture of Neo-Impressionism.

This picture, similar to the better-known *Railroad Embankment* of the same year, represents a shift towards Monet in
a period Angrand himself labeled "intermediate". In an
unpublished letter to a journalist in Rouen [Angrand
archives; the recipient is unnamed; the letter was apparently
written in March or early April, 1889], Angrand comments:
"I translated from nature then [1884–1885] only the
accidental aspects, and that by way of a picturesque and
varied brushwork. I indicate this tendency because of the
sudden change I am now obliged to confess which has led
me—with the help of intermediate studies [1886] owing a
debt to Monet: *Les Terrains vagues, L'Ile des ravageurs,
La Ligne de l'Ouest*—to my current researches [. . .]". These
same two periods are referred to by the critic Gustave Kahn
["Chronique de la Littérature et de l'Art", see above] when
The Seine at Saint-Ouen was exhibited at Georges Petit's:
"M. Angrand exhibits pictures that are three years old, in
which the picturesqueness of the brushwork and the happy
choice of motif show that this painter was close to a facile
success, were it not for the sincerity of his esthetic. In
transition [to the manner of 1887], a broad motif of the
Seine, blue, with a captivating horizon of trees".

The adherence already to Neo-Impressionist principles shows
in the opposition of orange and blue, the high horizon line,
the extreme simplicity of the composition, and the predilection for large areas of colloidal texture.

2

MAN AND WOMAN IN THE STREET (COUPLE DANS LA RUE). 1887.
Oil on canvas, 15 × 13″ (38 × 33 cm.).
Signed and dated l.l. "Ch. Angrand. 87".
Angrand list 25.

Collection Musée National d'Art Moderne, Paris.

The proximity to Seurat is evident, but more to his drawings of figures on the streets of Paris than to his paintings. By this year Angrand had fully accepted Neo-Impressionist color theory, and the colors are divided into their constituent hues. Local color is allowed to dominate, so that the dark blue color of the man's garment results principally from the blues themselves and their mixture on the palette with greens and reds. To provide a richer tone and to indicate other color reactions, quantities of green, red, violet, pink and orange are also used, but they are dominated by the blues. The absence of yellow which one would expect for sunlight is probably due to Angrand's fondness for grey tones.

3

THE GRAIN HARVEST [TRADITIONALLY: HAYSTACKS] (LES MEULES). 1887–1888.
Oil on canvas, 21 × 25″ (53.3 × 63.5 cm.).
Signed and dated l.l. "Ch. Angrand 88".

Early exhibitions: Paris, Georges Petit, "Exposition des 33", December 1887 – January 1888; Paris, Indépendants, 22 March – 3 May 1888, no. 20; Rouen, Galerie Legrip, August 1888; Probably Brussels, Les XX, February 1891, no. 2 ("La Moisson"); Probably Paris, Le Barc de Boutteville, November 1892.

Formerly Paul Signac; J. Selmersheim-Desgrange. Collection Mr. and Mrs. Morris Hadley, New York.

Although traditionally called "Haystacks", the picture clearly represents shocks of grain. It was exhibited in mid-winter 1887–1888, and was described by the Neo-Impressionists' friend, the Symbolist Gustave Kahn: "*Les Meules* gives evidence of a generous vision of plains inundated by the sun and ending in an abbreviated horizon which lets one calculate the languor and the slowness of the landscape". ["Chronique de la Littérature et de l'Art", see above.] Since the exhibition opened in December 1887, the picture must date from that

year. Perhaps the inscription was added much later and the artist forgot the year, or more likely, the picture might have been retouched for its two exhibitions in 1888 and accordingly dated.

In the unpublished letter of early 1889 (see remarks for no. 1), Angrand wrote of this picture:

■ The Harvest that M. Legrip exhibited is like the point of departure of my new orientation. And in it are found my present preoccupations of technique and esthetic.

This technique—superficially called 'pointillist' by many critics—is the division of tone, providing the easy and current application of the physical law of vision: laws of contrast and reaction. It is a simple question of profession, of means, but very important because intellectual evocation depends directly upon chromatic sensation.

I dream, in effect, of an art which would remain in the domain of sensation, and therefore, as it were, would be irreducible, one in which the coloring and the forms—colorings and forms wilfully chosen—would be in

[. . .] This is consequently to show you how little interest I have in the story-telling or genre element of these pictures which might be found amidst their generally matter-of-fact objectivity, in these landscapes which are, after all, only the inventory, the topographical nomenclature of the sites.

I think that a painting ought to reveal the sensory state of the man who signs it.

[. . . Our art is not] a flatly realistic art, a simple-minded copyist's work. No, it is, on the contrary, a synthetic and subjective art.

Angrand's letter and his painting together embody many preoccupations then current in Paris. His subject evokes Monet, who was painting stacks of hay at the same time, with a similar concern for aspects of color and light more than for the subject (Monet, however, would let the blue and blue-violet of the shadows show as one dominant tone, whereas Angrand stipples the blue with an intense red). His

composition harmonizes instead with the more geometric concerns of his fellow Neo-Impressionists, and with the group of painters then forming around Gauguin, later called the "Nabis". His insistence upon the "synthetic and subjective" aspects of his art also speaks for the generation of the Nabis and the Neo-Impressionists. Stacks of grain or hay seem a particularly appropriate subject for such a vantage point, since they show nature twice recast by man: first in the cultivation of the fields, then in the forming of the unnatural pyramids.

5

THE NORMAN FARM (SCENE DE METAIRIE NORMANDE). 1890.
Oil on canvas, 21 3/8 × 28 3/4" (54.2 × 73 cm.).
Signed and dated I.I. "Ch. Angrand. 90".
Angrand list 30.

Early exhibition: Probably Paris, Indépendants, 20 March – 27 April 1890, no. 11 ("Le Fumier").

Private collection, Paris.

In contrast to *The Grain Harvest* (no. 3), this scene is largely in shade and consequently has more even lighting and a very different coloring. The other picture arbitrarily darkens the field next to the lighted side of each stack, and lightens it next to the shaded side, to give a sense of the strong sunlight. Here there are no such contrasts, and the blue of indirect light enters into most areas. The unusual combination of blue, pink and the rather acid green make one regret that this is among the last pictures painted by Angrand before he turned to drawing, except for a brief return to oils in the Fauve period.

4
DAWN OVER THE SEINE (LA SEINE A L'AUBE). 1889.
Oil on canvas, 25 5/8 × 31 7/8" (65 × 81 cm.).
Signed and dated l.l. "Ch. Angrand — Paris — 89".
Angrand list 34.

Early exhibition: Perhaps Brussels, Les XX, February 1891,
no. 1 ("La Brume").

Collection Modern Art Foundation, Oscar Ghez, Geneva.

A logical outgrowth of the earlier *Seine at Saint-Ouen*
(no. 1), this extraordinary picture carries Neo-Impressionism
to one extreme: a nearly uniform colloidal texture. Monet and
Turner earlier, in similar subjects, used veils of translucent
paint through which one looks, and these veils remain like
damp sheets, stretched across the surface. Angrand uses
instead an aggregate of small particles of indefinite spatial
position, corresponding to the fine drops of moisture in a
real fog.

6

SELF-PORTRAIT (PORTRAIT DE L'ARTISTE). 1892.
Conté crayon, 24 × 17 1/2" (61 × 44.5 cm.).
Signed and dated l.r. "Ch. Angrand. 92".
Angrand list 148.

The Lehman Collection, New York.

This wonderful self-portrait should be compared with
Seurat's drawing of Signac (no. 88). In both cases we see
the elegance professed deliberately by Signac, Angrand and
the Neo-Impressionists as a witty counterpoint to the
bohemianism of many of their friends. Angrand's drawing,
like Seurat's, shares in the preference for velvety chiaroscuro
that was common to Fantin-Latour, Redon, Carrière and
others active in the 1880s and 1890s, in opposition to the
very flat tones used by the Nabis.

7

FARMYARD IN NORMANDY (LE CLOS NORMAND).
c. 1907.
Oil on canvas, 31 1/8 × 38 1/4" (79 × 97 cm.).
Angrand list 3.

Collection Pierre Angrand, Paris.

From about 1901 to 1908, Angrand returned to painting and
produced a few pictures that share in the second flowering
of Neo-Impressionism in the Fauve period. It is unlikely that
these pictures, which could not have been seen by many
artists, were themselves influential at the time, but they have
a quality of abstraction that is as close, perhaps, to Kupka of
1910–1911 as to Cross and Signac of 1906–1908. It
requires some concentration to find the two figures picking
apples amongst the greens and ruddy reds. Angrand had long
been preoccupied by the necessity of organizing a painting
by purely pictorial rules, not by subject matter. In an undated
letter to Cross of about 1903 [Signac archives], he wrote:
"I think like you that one can pluck nothing out of exactitude.
In order to reach an expressive goal, one must create the
harmony that leads there, regardless of any deformations that
result".

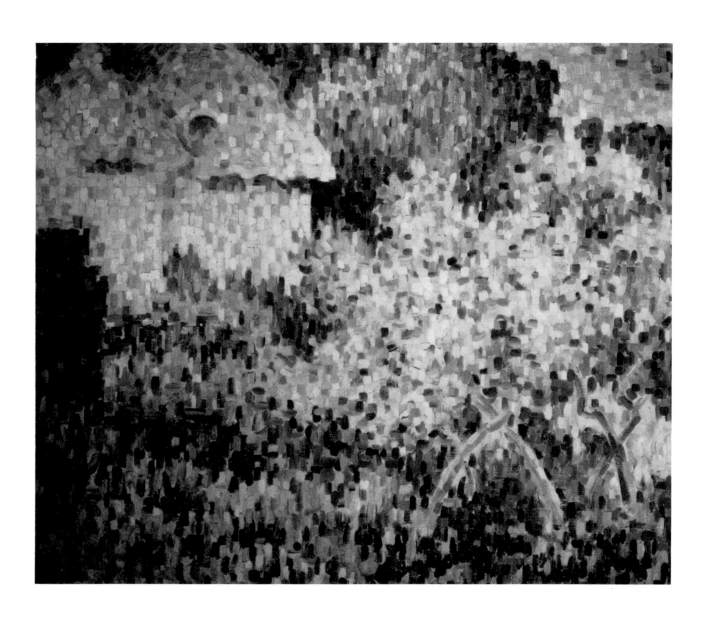

8

TUGBOAT STEAM (LA FUMEE DU REMORQUEUR).
c. 1914.
Conté crayon, 16 7/8 × 24 3/4″ (43 × 63 cm.).
Stamped l.l. ''Ch. Angrand''.
Angrand list 143.

Collection Pierre Angrand, Paris.

The rounded and expansive forms here are the opposite of
the stabbing gestures of Seurat's *Drawbridge* (no. 66), even
though there is in both a love of tonal value and ambiguity
of plane that recall Piranesi. Pierre Angrand [BIBLI-
OGRAPHY 2] writes: ''The drawings of Seurat possess rigor,
depth, power; those of Angrand have mystery, penetration,
grace. The former compel attention by a kind of arrested
tumult and equilibrated fervor, the latter are inclined toward
melancholy or tenderness. The former are clouds of dusky
powder, the latter are all evanescence''.

9

THE FOX'S RAID (LE RENARD EN MARAUDE). c. 1915.
Pastel, 24 3/8 × 34 1/4" (62 × 87 cm.).
Signed l.r. "Charles Angrand".
Angrand list 317.

Collection Pierre Angrand, Paris.

Until about 1910, Angrand worked principally in conté
crayon and charcoal. Perhaps inspired by his return to oil
painting he then began to use colored chalks, and his large
pastels are in the lineage of Daumier and Millet, whose
works they recall both in subject and in form.

10
AGED TREES (LES VIEUX ARBRES). c. 1920.
Pastel, 21 × 27 3/4″ (53.5 × 70.5 cm.).
Signed l.l. ''Ch. Angrand''.
Angrand list 302.

Collection Pierre Angrand, Paris.

11
ENTRANCE TO THE VILLAGE (L'ENTRÉE DU VILLAGE).
c. 1920.
Pastel, 17 3/4 × 23 5/8" (45 × 60 cm.).
Angrand list 308.

Collection Pierre Angrand, Paris.

Henri-Edmond Cross
(1856–1910)

Although five years older than Seurat, Cross did not become a Neo-Impressionist until after his colleague's death in 1891, and his art belongs to the later history of Neo-Impressionism. (Born Delacroix, he changed his name to the English equivalent.) After youthful studies in Lille, Cross settled in Paris in 1881 and exhibited in the official Salon. A founding member of the Indépendants in 1884, his *Monaco* of that year, with its smoothly-brushed but intense yellows and greens, shows that he was close to Bastien-Lepage with an admixture of Manet. Until Seurat's death, Cross was friendly to the Neo-Impressionists but did not share their style. In that year he left Paris for the south of France, establishing himself first at Cabasson, then at Saint-Clair on the coast, where he lived until his death in 1910. 1891 was also the year in which he produced his first fully Neo-Impressionist works, and thereafter he was one of the major figures of the group. He was especially intimate with Signac, who lived at Saint-Tropez, not far from Saint-Clair, but very close also to Angrand, Luce, Van Rysselberghe and Fénéon, to all of whom he sent his often anguished, always beautiful letters.

Cross was something of an introvert, but endowed with a rare charm, and immensely cultured. His letters and note-books are full of sensitive references to Carlyle, Emerson, Nietzsche and others. Starting about 1895, he began an integral translation of Ruskin's *Elements of Drawing* for Signac, who was then preparing his *D'Eugène Delacroix au Néo-Impressionnisme* (1898–1899) in which the British writer is featured. By 1895 also, Cross began to write more frequently of the dilemma to which he was always very sensitive: the conflict between the abstract color-components of a painting and its natural images. Together with Signac, he developed the second Neo-Impressionist style of large, mosaic-like strokes that entered prominently into the formulation both of Fauvism and of Cubism. Cross shared with Signac the duties of host to their many acquaintances who came to the Midi to visit them. Most of the Fauves —Matisse, Derain, Puy, Valtat, Manguin, Camoin, Marquet— came frequently to Saint-Clair and Saint-Tropez, and they all passed through important Neo-Impressionist phases. Cross managed to bear with severe arthritis that sometimes immobilized him, but he limited his travels to annual trips to Paris, and to two visits to Italy, in 1903 and 1908. By the time of his death, his work stood as a hymn of praise to color and sunlight, and helped form the vision of the Mediterranean coast which is commonplace today.

Cross showed at the Salon in Paris in 1881; in 1884 he began exhibiting with the Indépendants and continued there regularly until his death. In addition to taking part in all exhibitions devoted to Neo-Impressionism from 1892 onward, he was given one-man shows by Druet in 1905, by Bernheim-Jeune in 1907, 1910, and 1913, by the Indépendants and La Libre Esthétique (Brussels) in 1911, Bernheim-Jeune again in 1923–1924, Jacques Rodriguès-Henriquès in 1926, Galerie Dru in 1927, Bernheim-Jeune in 1937, Jacques Dubourg in 1950, Fine Arts Associates (New York) in 1951, and the Bibliothèque Municipale de Douai, in 1956.

Major paintings not in this exhibition include *Monaco*, 1884 (Musée de Douai); *Portrait of Madame Cross*, 1891 (Musée d'Art Moderne, Paris); *Plage de Baigne-Cul*, 1891–1892 (Mrs. W. E. Josten, New York); *Harvest*, 1892 (Mr. and Mrs. John Hay Whitney, New York); *Les Iles d'Or*, c. 1892 (Musée d'Art Moderne, Paris); *La Plage Ombragée* 1902 (formerly Count Kessler); *Rio di Noale, Venice*, 1903–1904 (Robert Marseille, Paris); *Ponte San Trovaso, Venice*, 1903–1905 (Rijksmuseum Kröller-Müller, Otterlo); *Le Bois*, 1906–1907 (Musée de l'Annonciade, Saint-Tropez).

Bibliography: See BIBLIOGRAPHY 1, 9, 20, 23, 24, 26, 27, 28 and Charles Angrand, "Henri-Edmond Cross", *Les Temps Nouveaux*, vol. 16, no. 5, 23 July 1910, p. 7; Isabelle Compin, *Henri-Edmond Cross* [Catalogue raisonné], Paris, 1964; "Henri-Edmond Cross", in BIBLIOGRAPHY 2; Lucie Cousturier, "H.E. Cross", *L'Art Décoratif* vol. 29, March 1913, pp. 117–132, reprinted in book form, Paris, 1932; Maurice Denis, "Henri-Edmond Cross", catalogue of exhibition, Bernheim-Jeune, 22 April – 8 May 1907, reprinted several times, and "Henri-Edmond Cross", catalogue of exhibition. Bernheim-Jeune, 17 October – 5 November 1910; Félix Fénéon (ed.), "Le dernier carnet d'Henri-Edmond Cross" and "Inédits d'Henri-Edmond Cross", *Bulletin de la Vie Artistique*, vol. 3, nos. 10–20, 15 May – 15 October 1922; Emile Verhaeren, "Henri-Edmond Cross", *La Nouvelle Revue Française*, July 1910, reprinted in *Sensations*, Paris, 1927, pp. 204–208.

"Compin catalogue" in the individual picture entries refers to the catalogue raisonné listed above.

12

THE SHORE AT LA VIGNASSE (PLAGE DE LA VIGNASSE).
1891–1892.
Oil on canvas, 25 5/8 × 36 1/4" (65 × 92 cm.).
Signed l.l. "Henri Edmond Cross".
Compin catalogue 32.

Early exhibitions: Paris, Indépendants, 19 March – 27 April
1892, no. 311; Probably Paris, Le Barc de Boutteville,
"Deuxième Exposition des Peintres Impressionnistes et
Symbolistes", May 1892; Paris, Hôtel Brébant, "Exposition
des Peintres Néo-Impressionnistes", 2 December 1892 –
8 January 1893, no. 4; Antwerp, L'Association pour l'Art,
May 1893, no. 4.

Formerly Olivier Senn.
Private collection, Paris.

Cross was nearly 40 before he developed his own variant of
Neo-Impressionism. It was only in 1891, the year this picture
was begun, that he forsook a rather traditional, light-struck
naturalism for the divided color and dotted facture of Signac
and the others. The abruptness of the change is shown by the
fact that he did not go through a period in which the small
strokes are interrelated so as to preserve a balance with his

customary nuance of gradation. Instead, the wafers of
pigment are applied with complete arbitrariness. They are
seized upon for their independent, decorative qualities to an
extreme not seen in the work of any other Neo-Impressionist
at this date. The background is close to *Les Iles d'Or* of the
same time, but here the power of sunlight is such that the
whites are allowed to dominate. In the foreground, too,
despite the highly unusual greens and other pastel tones, the
colors are mixed with white to produce a blanched effect.
Later [nos. 19 and 20] he will develop the opposite concept,
in which sunlight will intensify, rather than bleach the colors.

13

ROCKY SHORE NEAR ANTIBES (CALANQUE DES
ANTIBOIS). 1891–1892.
Oil on canvas, 25 3/4 × 36 1/2″ (65.4 × 92.7 cm.).
Signed l.r. "Henri Edmond Cross".
Compin catalogue 33.

Early exhibitions: Paris, Indépendants, 19 March – 27 April
1892, no. 314; Probably Paris, Le Barc de Boutteville,
"Deuxième Exposition des Peintres Impressionnistes et
Symbolistes", 1892; Paris, Hôtel Brébant, "Exposition des
Peintres Néo-Impressionnistes", 2 December 1892 –
8 January 1893, no. 13; Brussels, Les XX, February 1893,
no. 5; Antwerp, L'Association pour l'Art, May 1893, no. 5.

Formerly Zborowski; R. Baudoin.
Collection Mr. and Mrs. John Hay Whitney, New York.

In the previous picture, the frequent use of oranges with
blues, and yellows with violets, indicates Cross's concern for
Neo-Impressionist color theory. Here, on the other hand,
only the shadows with their juxtapositions of reds and blues
would seem to embody theory. The emphasis instead is upon
the almost obsessively regular discs of pigment which, in
water, mountain and sky, seem to result from some system of
actual measurement.

14

CASCADING HAIR (LA CHEVELURE). c. 1892.   43
Oil on canvas, 24 × 18 1/8″ (61 × 46 cm.).
Stamped l.l. "H. E. Cross".
Compin catalogue 37.

Lent by Galerie Lorenceau, Paris.

The most extreme of Cross's inventions of the 1891–1893
period, both for the starkness of the composition with its
provocative hiding of the face, and also for the shower of
colored wafers. Japanese prints, of which he frequently
writes, lie behind such a picture.

15

THE FARM, MORNING (LA FERME, MATIN; LES
BOUILLEURS DE CRU). 1892–1893.
Oil on canvas, 25 1/2 × 36 1/8" (65 × 92 cm.).
Signed and dated l.l. "93. Henri Edm. Cross".
Compin catalogue 40.

Early exhibitions: Paris, Indépendants, 18 March – 27 April
1893, no. 319; Brussels, La Libre Esthétique, 23 February –
1 April 1895, no. 118.

Formerly Henri Matisse.
Collection Jean Matisse, Pontoise.

Cross's continued inventiveness is shown in the strong
rhythms generated by the trees, rhythms which are found
also in Signac's work of the same period, for both participate
in the development of Art Nouveau. This picture, like several
of Signac's, confesses an admiration of Puvis de Chavannes
and a wish to conceive paintings as wall decorations. Except
for the yellow foliage behind the purple tree trunks, the
coloration is built more upon harmony than contrast. The
trees are cork-oaks, as can be deduced from the horizontal
bands on the trunks; the figures are boiling grape mash.

Matisse owned this picture, and its swaying curves reappear

in his famous *Joy of Life* (Barnes Foundation). It is not
known when he obtained it, but it is likely that it was about
1904–1905 when he was closest to Cross. Cross, in turn,
owned three Matisse oils [Cross to Angrand, 28 December
1907, Angrand archives; the pictures not identified but
antedating 1906], and perhaps an exchange of their paintings
was involved.

16

THE FARM, EVENING (LA FERME, SOIR). 1892–1893.
Oil on canvas, 25 1/8 × 36 1/4" (65 × 92 cm.).
Signed and dated l.l. "93. Henri Edmond Cross".
Compin catalogue 39.

Early exhibitions: Paris, Indépendants, 18 March – 27 April
1893, no. 318; Brussels, La Libre Esthétique, 23 February –
1 April 1895, no. 117.

Formerly Paul Signac.
Private collection, Paris.

A pendant to the previous picture and, like it, owned by an
artist: it was in Signac's possession shortly after its
completion.

17

THE BEACH AT SAINT-CLAIR (LA PLAGE DE SAINT-CLAIR). 1901.
Oil on canvas, 26 3/4 × 36 1/4" (68 × 92 cm.).
Signed and dated l.l. "Henri Edmond Cross 1901".
Compin catalogue 96.

Formerly C. Cherfils; Paul Signac.
Private collection, Paris.

The pictures of the early 1890s were harmonized by analogy (to use the proper Neo-Impressionist phrase). *The Farm, Morning*, for example, has related greens, blues and yellows for foliage, and violets and blues for the tree trunks. By the turn of the century, harmony by contrast, which had long been Signac's method, enters prominently into Cross's palette. Yellow and lavender complementaries dominate the foreground in this painting, and the hues are each more intense than before. Still, however, transitional colors are used to soften the contrasts.

Cross's nudes along the Mediterranean coast were important forebears of the nymphs that appear a few years later in Fauve paintings. It is such pictures as this that Matisse was particularly impressed by, and his *Luxe, Calme et Volupté* [no. 159] is its direct descendant. Like the other Neo-Impressionists, Cross was an Anarchist-Communist, but his modest interest in peasant life had given way to visions of sensuous beauty. "A long time ago," he wrote van Rysselberghe about 1905 [Van Rysselberghe archives],

■ I discovered my insensitivity towards the peasant. I find him here [in the south] especially without plastic interest, and I would not know how to paint him. He only moves me as a spot, and he seems small and far away. On the rocks, on the sand of the beaches, under the clumps of pine, nymphs and naiads appear to me, a whole world born of beautiful light.

These beautiful forms have circulated in my vision too long for me not to attempt to render them perceptible by painting.

The world of painting as imagination is made even more explicit in Cross's notebooks [*Bulletin de la Vie Artistique*, see above].

■ A wise man is, according to Nietszche, a *creator of*

■ *values.* That is the great task. Nothing, in effect, has value *in itself;* the world of reality is unconcerned matter which only has the interest that we give it. The true philosopher is thus the man whose personality is strong enough to create *the world which interests man.*

18
STUDY FOR "LE CAP NEGRE" (SAINT-CLAIR, LES
COLLINES). 1906.
Watercolor, 6 3/4 × 4 3/4" (17 × 12 cm.).
Stamped l.r. "H.E.C.".

Private collection, Paris.

This watercolor can be identified as a study for the left side
of no. 10. From Cross's many letters and his notebooks, we
know how such a study worked with the oil. First he would
establish a chromatic harmony, merely a set of colors that he
wished to develop. Then he would give it a tentative
compositional form, drawing upon memory and prior
sketches for the natural imagery. At this point he would seek
out the motif in nature, and this watercolor represents that
stage. However, far from copying nature, such watercolors
embody what he called "sacrifices", which took the form
both of omissions and simplifications. Often they were
completed in the studio on the basis of light pencil sketches
and mere touches of color done on the spot. He wrote to
Lucie Cousturier ["Henri-Edmond Cross", see above]:

■ I compose in the studio, coming as close as possible to
my interior vision; then, the harmony being established,

■ partly on paper and canvas, and partly in my head, I set
about making my sensations objective—sensations
corresponding to the initial vision—in front of nature.
These documentary sketches, during the definitive
execution of the painting, more often than not are
behind me or in a filing box.

In making his sensations "objective", Cross was always
conscious of the materials he worked with [*Bulletin de la Vie
Artistique*, see above]:

■ [Painters'] materials permit a particular thought, and not
others. Working in front of nature does not permit the
deepest study of these materials:
The material for itself, treated in such a way that it
gives beauty at the same time that it remains adequate
to the plastic thought.

19
LE CAP NEGRE. 1906.
Oil on canvas, 35 1/2 × 46" (90 × 117 cm.).
Signed l.r. "Henri Edmond Cross".
Compin catalogue 151.

Early exhibitions: Paris, Bernheim-Jeune, 22 April – 8 May 1907, no. 1; Paris, Bernheim-Jeune, 24 February – 7 March 1913, no. 44; Paris, Bernheim-Jeune, "Collection Herbert Kullmann," May 1914, no. 4.

Formerly Prince de Wagram; J. Laroche; A. Sommaruga; Herbert Kullmann.
Collection Mr. and Mrs. William B. Jaffe, New York.

The full flowering of Cross's style in the Fauve period is found in this picture. Based entirely now upon strong contrasts, having still less to do with natural color, it has an intensity of hue that is hardly exceeded by the Fauves themselves. Lucie Cousturier writes of this picture ["Henri-Edmond Cross", see above]:

■ This purely painterly imagination bursts forth with oriental exhuberance in *Paysage avec le Cap Nègre*, a new and magnificent page which reveals, not

■ Provence, but tumultuous pleasures, not languor, but excesses, because it is not graduated tones this time, it is contrasts which abound; without waiting for the conventional heavy foregrounds, a red peak throws against the yellow-green sky its eloquent phrase, dominating both the poignant clamors of sulfur trees which are irritated by pink, and shaded with ultramarine blue, and also orange trees shaded with green and blue-green, underlined by cherry pink and purple [. . .] It is everything modern music has found of the rarest and boldest in dissonances and postponed resolutions. It is no longer a rendering of light, tree or soil, it is a bold transposition of these into the abstract language of tints, in which each, in different degrees excited, solidified, weakened, possesses infinite expressive virtues.

20

GARDEN IN PROVENCE (LE JARDIN ROUGE; PAYSAGE MEDITERRANEE). 1906–1907.
Oil on canvas, 28 3/4 × 36 1/4″ (73 × 92 cm.).
Signed l.r. "Henri Edmond Cross".
Compin catalogue 164.

Early exhibitions: Paris, Bernheim-Jeune, 22 April – 8 May 1907, no. 10; Brighton, Public Art Galleries, "Exhibition of the Work of Modern French Artists", 10 June – 31 August 1910, no. 150; Paris, Bernheim-Jeune, 17 October – 5 November 1910, no. 15; Paris, Bernheim-Jeune, 24 February – 7 March 1913, no. 19.

Formerly Alphonse Kann.
Collection Charles R. Lachman, New York.

The violent mixture of a passionate love of nature (or, rather, the feelings nature engenders), a sensual immersion in raw pigment itself, and a nearly mathematical control over the whole, is nowhere better seen than in this painting. Its origin was spontaneous [Cross to Van Rysselberghe, 17 June 1906, van Rysselberghe archives]:

■ I should have written you earlier. It is not because
    I haven't thought of it, but my infantile and violent need

■ to paint took over everything, and as soon as I could
    get a palette, I went to the nearest spot—the garden—in
    order to prove to myself that I still knew how to put a
    green next to a red, and especially to satisfy this feeling,
    this rutting which only painters know. This garden is
    all red—the flames of the geraniums which over-
    stimulate the blue-green of the mimosas. It is in the
    midst of these ardors that I find calm.

The abstract, and yet fully sensuous impact of Cross' color was evident to his contemporaries, witness Maurice Denis' review of the same painting [exhibition catalogue 1907, see above]:

■ Here is a dark entrance to a garden. It is fiercely hot:
    the light one sees in the background evokes the
    heaviness of the south. But the subject is in shadow:
    it is everything that takes place sheltered from raw
    daylight, the conflict of somber reds with deep greens,
    and the greens going to blue. The presence of violet is
    fortunately avoided, because it would explode in this
    major scale; and in a pure contrast of color, the greens
    rejoin the reds which, nonetheless intense, trumpet to
    the geraniums and grow fainter by the tree trunks.

21
TREES AT SAINT-CLAIR, c. 1906–1908.
Charcoal, 8 7/8 × 10 1/4" (22.7 × 26.2 cm.).
Stamped l.r. "H.E.C.".

Collection Mr. and Mrs. Hugo Perls, New York.

22
ROCKY SHORE AT AGAY (LES ROCHERS D'AGAY).
c. 1907–1908.
Watercolor, 6 5/8 × 9 3/8" (17 × 24 cm.).
Signed l.r. "HE. C.".

Private collection, Paris.

Among his self-addressed aphorisms [*Bulletin de la Vie Artistique*, see above], Cross recorded: "Watercolor. A form of writing. The great role played by the paper. The Japanese". Although we know that the rocks at Agay are really red (they were painted by Guillaumin and Valtat, as well), we also are aware of the arbitrary way Cross lets the medium express itself. The liquid strokes move across the paper to reveal it; orange and blue, yellow and violet are brought together; the structure has the firmness of Japanese prints.

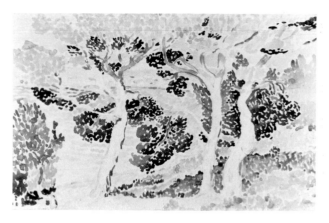

23
THE ARTIST'S GARDEN AT SAINT-CLAIR (LE JARDIN
DE L'ARTISTE A SAINT-CLAIR). c. 1908.
Watercolor, 10 1/2 × 14″ (26.6 × 35.8 cm.).
Signed l.l. "HE. C.".

Formerly Félix Fénéon.
Collection The Metropolitan Museum of Art,
Harris Brisbane Dick Fund, 1948.

24
TREES (LE BRUSC). 1909.
Watercolor, 12 × 18″ (27 × 43 cm.).
Signed and dated l.l. "Henri Edmond Cross. 1909".
Compin catalogue "S", p. 345.

Collection J. P. Durand-Matthiesen, Geneva.

In late 1908 or early 1909, Cross wrote these aphorisms
[*Bulletin de la Vie Artistique*, see above]:

■ Not the object itself, but a transfiguration based on a
concordance of lines, a harmony of color. A certain
beautiful form embellished by certain magnificent colors
will interest us: it might be that it corresponds to a tree.

Forms, colors make allusions to objects, The thing that
I want to represent, is myself.

These trees, these mountains, this sea, they are myself.

53

Albert Dubois-Pillet

(1846–1890)

Louis Auguste Albert Dubois was born in Paris (later he added his mother's maiden name), but grew up in Toulouse. He graduated from Saint-Cyr in 1867, and was stationed in a number of cities before settling in Paris in 1880, where he was attached to the Garde Républicaine. He was entirely self-taught as an artist. In 1877 and 1879 the official Salon accepted still lifes from him, but his submissions from 1880 through 1884 were uniformly rejected. Because he was a military officer, it has been tempting to regard Dubois-Pillet as the Douanier Rousseau of Neo-Impressionism. This is misleading, however, not only because of Dubois-Pillet's sophisticated bearing and a temperament like that of an articulate lawyer, but also because the somewhat "primitive" characteristics of his paintings were qualities deliberately sought. That this is so is evident from his pictures of 1884–1885, which disclose a fresh and entirely skillful naturalism. Even the earlier *Dead Child* of 1881 (whose exhibition in 1884 inspired Zola to give it to his imaginary painter, Claude Lantier) is the work of a professional artist lacking all naïveté. Dubois-Pillet met Seurat, Angrand, and Signac in 1884 when the Indépendants was founded. Not only did he write the statutes for the group, but he remained until 1888 the chief organizer within it for the Neo-Impressionists. In the early days of the Indépendants, his studio-apartment at 19 Quai Saint-Michel was its unofficial headquarters. Recent researches by Lily Bazalgette and Dr. J. Sutter have shown that Dubois-Pillet exploited his friendships with fellow Masons on the Paris city councils (then strongly anticlerical) to win favorable exhibition terms for the Indépendants. Dubois-Pillet exhibited regularly with the Indépendants until his death and, also in Nantes in 1886 and in Brussels with Les XX in 1888 and 1890. He was transferred to Le Puy in December, 1889, and died there in August, 1890. A fire subsequently destroyed a great many of his paintings, and the resultant loss has made him an even more mysterious painter than otherwise might have been true. The surviving pictures, and those listed in contemporaneous exhibitions, are dominated by views along the Seine, particularly the commercial quays in Paris.

Although he has been included in nearly all exhibitions devoted to Neo-Impressionism, Dubois-Pillet was only twice given one-man shows, at the offices of the *Revue Indépendante* in the autumn of 1888, and at the Indépendants in the spring of 1891.

Paintings not in the present exhibition are *Dead Child*, 1881 (Musée Crozatier, Le Puy); *The Artist's Studio*, 1884 (Musée de Saint-Etienne); *Le Quai de Bercy*, 1885 (Musée Crozatier, Le Puy); *The Lamp*, c. 1887 (René Leuck, Paris); *Portrait of a Young Woman in White Dress*, c. 1888–1889 (Musée de Saint-Etienne); *River's Edge in Winter*, c. 1889 (Mr. and Mrs. Arthur G. Altschul, New York).

Bibliography: See BIBLIOGRAPHY 1, 3, 15, 23, 26, 29, and Lily Bazalgette, "A. Dubois-Pillet" in BIBLIOGRAPHY 2; Jules Antoine, "Dubois-Pillet", *La Plume*, vol. 3, no. 56, 1 September 1891, p. 299; Jules Christophe, "Dubois-Pillet", *Les Hommes d'Aujourd'hui*, vol. 8, no. 370, 1890; Félix Fénéon, "Treize Toiles et Quatre Dessins de M. Albert Dubois-Pillet", *La Revue Indépendante*, vol. 9, no. 24, October 1888, pp. 134–137.

27

THE SEINE AT PARIS. c. 1888.
Oil on canvas, 31 1/2 × 39" (79.9 × 99.5 cm.).
Signed l.r. "duBois-Pillet".

Formerly Private collection, Le Puy; Dr. Jean Sutter.
Collection Mr. and Mrs. Arthur G. Altschul, New York.

Dubois-Pillet was perhaps following Camille Pissarro in his
preference for the commercial life of the Seine (he also, like
Pissarro, painted similar sites at Rouen) and other rivers.
This picture is particularly close to the later Thames scene
by Georges Lemmen [no. 130] and related subjects were
painted by Luce and others. That such a motif would become
one of the most common in Neo-Impressionism is quite
appropriate, in view of the attractions that water, steam and
sky offer to artists concerned with complexities of color, and
also because of its "modern" character.

The buildings and the bridge are sufficiently generalized to
make impossible a precise location of the site, but it might be
the Quai Henri IV looking upriver, towards the Bercy district
(such a picture was exhibited at the Indépendants in 1890,
no. 320). The picture dated 1885, *Le Quai de Bercy*, is a
view downriver towards the Quai Henri IV, that is, in the

opposite direction. It has a similar bridge and at the same
spot, a similar pavilion roof (undoubtedly one of the many
pavilion-warehouses of the area).

25

LE PONT DES ARTS (LES QUAIS). 1886–1888.
Ink on buff-colored paper, 6 1/2 × 6″ (16.5 × 15.2 cm.).

Collection Mr. and Mrs. Arthur G. Altschul, New York.

The bridge in the background is the Pont des Arts and,
beyond it, the spire of Sainte-Chapelle and the twin towers
of Notre-Dame are on the left, the dome of the Institut de
France on the far right. Dubois-Pillet, Seurat, Signac [no. 91],
Camille Pissarro [no. 49] and other Neo-Impressionists did
drawings formed of dots of ink.

26

ROOF TOPS AND THE TOWERS OF SAINT-SULPICE
(LES TOURS SAINT-SULPICE). 1887.
Oil on canvas, 32 × 23 1/2″ (81.3 × 60 cm.).
Signed l.l. "duBois-Pillet".

Early exhibitions: Brussels, Les XX, February 1888, no. 4;
Paris, Indépendants (Dubois-Pillet retrospective), 20 March –
27 April 1891, no. 441.

Collection Walter P. Chrysler, Jr., New York.

There were two paintings of identical title in the exhibition
of Les XX in 1888 but in an unpublished letter to Octave
Maus of December 19, 1887 [BIBLIOGRAPHY 26], Dubois-
Pillet listed the dimensions of his pictures with their frames.
No. 4 is recorded as 85 × 105 cm., which would suit the
present picture with a frame five inches wide.

The small dots of paint complete an evolution to fully-
fledged Neo-Impressionism which began in 1886, when
Dubois-Pillet began dividing his color, using at first a soft
and varied brushstroke recalling Camille Pissarro.

28

SAINT-MICHEL D'AIGUILHE IN THE SNOW (EFFET DE NEIGE). 1889.
Oil on canvas, 23 5/8 × 14 3/8″ (60 × 37 cm.).
Signed l.l. "duBois-Pillet".

Early exhibitions: Paris, Indépendants, 20 March – 27 April 1890, no. 322.

Collection Musée Crozatier, Le Puy-en-Velay, France.

Léo Gausson
(1860–1944)

Louis Léon Gausson was born on February 14, 1860, and lived until October 27, 1944 (and not 1942 as commonly reported). The evidence of his surviving work, however, seems to prove that he was a painter of high quality only for a handful of years. He was born at Lagny-sur-Marne, just east of Paris, the fifth child of a prosperous merchant couple. At an early age he studied engraving with Théophile Chauvel, and then entered the shop of Eugène Froment, devoted to woodcuts used widely for illustrations. Maximilien Luce was a fellow worker at Froment's. In 1883, they were both thrown out of work by the rapidly spreading zincograph process (just as mechanical equipment had earlier put Renoir on the streets, when his hand-painted porcelain work foundered), and they then turned to painting. Gausson later stated that Cavallo-Peduzzi and Antonio Cortès were his teachers. Together with Cavallo, Gausson and Luce formed what Dr. Jean Sutter has called the "Lagny group", and they shared studios off and on for several years in Lagny and in Montmartre. Gausson's first public exhibition seems to have been the Salon of 1886, which accepted a plaster medallon of his. In 1887 he began to show paintings with the Indépendants, and continued to do so trough 1895. He was given his only one-man exhibition at the Galeries Laffitte in 1896, but after that his activity seems to have diminished steadily. In 1899 and 1900 he showed drawings, paintings, sculptures and jewelry in the Lagny salon, but thereafter he painted seldom and in an irregular manner. He did a good many engravings before the turn of the century, including several after Millet. From 1901 to 1908 he travelled in Africa and stayed for a long time at Conakry. The balance of his life was spent in minor government posts. Gausson's work seems to have been best from 1886 to about 1890. He then began to flirt with the styles of other artists and, perhaps through his friendship with the poet Adolphe Retté (whose books he illustrated), he adopted a "Symbolist" manner close to that of the Nabis. His landscapes remained his most interesting work but softened with smoothly-brushed tones and the gradual abandonment of the color and texture of Neo-Impressionism. None of his paintings are well-known, and they often appear now with the forged signatures of Dubois-Pillet or Luce. His sketches directly after nature were regarded by Fénéon as his best paintings.

Gausson was included in the earliest exhibitions devoted to Neo-Impressionism, but was usually omitted from such shows between the wars. Aside from his regular appearances at the Indépendants from 1887 to 1895, he showed at Le Barc de Boutteville in 1891, the first Salon of the Rosecrucians the same year, with Les XX in Brussels in 1892, L'Association pour l'Art in Antwerp in 1893, at the Théâtre Antoine in 1899, and had his only one-man show at the Galeries Laffitte, Paris, in March and April, 1896.

Principal pictures not in the exhibition include *The Church at Gouvernes*, 1886–1887 (V. W. van Gogh, Laren); *Evening Landscape*, c. 1890 (Dr. Dulon, Beauchamp); *Village, Seine-et-Marne*, 1891 (Private collection, Paris); *The Church at Eragny*, 1891 (J. Sutter, Paris).

Bibliography: See BIBLIOGRAPHY 1, 18, 22, 23, 26, and Jean Sutter and Pierre Eberhart, "Léo Gausson" in BIBLIOGRAPHY 2, and Félix Fénéon, "Léo Gausson", *La Revue Blanche*, vol. 10, April 1896, p. 336.

29

RIVER LANDSCAPE AT LAGNY (RIVIERE ET PONT
A LAGNY-SUR-MARNE). 1886.
Oil on canvas, 24 × 32 1/4" (61 × 82 cm.).
Signed and dated l.r. "Léo Gausson 1886".

Given by the artist as a wedding gift to the present owner,
daughter of the architect-painter Georges Tardif, intimate
friend of Gausson and Luce.

Collection Tardif-Fonteneau, Paris.

Only Seurat and Signac painted pictures in 1886 whose
division of color was carried as far as in this landscape by
Gausson. The trees are dominated by orange and yellow
in the light areas, representing the force of sunlight which
overwhelms the local color, and by blue and green in the
shade, where the local color is strong and is fortified by the
blue of indirect light (and this is conveniently also the
opposite of the sun's orange). Blue and orange, largely
segregated in the trees, are brought together in the planes
of the houses facing left to form an unresolved, vibrating
juxtaposition which does not "mix in the eye"—for the
painter did not wish it to.

30
FOREST SCENE (SOUS-BOIS). 1888.
Oil on wood, 12 1/2 × 10 1/2" (31.7 × 26.7 cm.).
Signed l.r. "Léo Gausson 1888".

Lent by Wildenstein & Co., Inc., New York.

In the more regular, choppy brushwork of two years later,
Gausson maintains the unmixed vibration of hues of his
1886 landscape. The grass is composed of several colors,
including blue and pink, but is dominated by oranges and
greens which retain their separate identities. The orange is
further exalted by its color opposite, the blue dominant of the
tree trunks. This blue, in turn, has a sprinkling of the grass's
oranges and pinks to excite the eye, and hence the painting
is a melody brought into harmony by the adjustment of
contrasts.

Louis Hayet
(1864–1940)

Like Luce, Hayet was self-taught and, because he was poor, he worked as an artisan for many years before he became a painter. At the age of twelve he left school to support himself, and two years later was a painter in a construction firm, following his father's profession. He travelled and worked in Normandy and the Paris region, doing watercolors and drawings on the side. By 1883 he had met Lucien Pissarro in Pontoise, and they remained close friends until about 1895. Although continuing his trade of painter-decorator, Hayet was ever more absorbed by color theory and painting. He had found some of his father's notes on Chevreul's color theory in 1881 (the same year Seurat was reading Ogden Rood), and in the period 1881–1886, his researches seem to have paralleled those of Seurat. He had met Signac in 1885, and in 1886 Seurat whom he "followed" for a year, according to a letter he later wrote Signac [Signac archives]. From September 1886 to the following September, Hayet was stationed at Versailles for his military service. He maintained contact with the Pissarros, and prepared elaborate color charts in his continued researches in theory. The three years following his release from service were the most extraordinary of his career. He was active in the society of the Neo-Impressionist painters and their friends among the young Symbolist writers and musicians, and he produced the largest number of his finest watercolors, gouaches and paintings.

A virtual alchemist in his devotion to unusual techniques and to theory, Hayet was aptly labeled by Camille Pissarro as "very dreamy and very practical". He offered advice to his comrades on various technical procedures in the graphic arts and painting [Lucien Pissarro archives], produced unusual paintings on cloth, and preferred his own encaustic mixtures to traditional oils. At the same time, he was intensely moody, often jealous, and repeatedly broke with his Neo-Impressionist friends. After 1891 he maintained contact with Lucien Pissarro (and visited him in London), but even that was over by about 1895 and he lived thereafter in relative isolation. In the 1890s he went through a phase in which he was close to Monticelli, of whom he wrote to Lucien. He did some decorations for the Théâtre Français in 1894, perhaps through his friendship with Lugné-Poë. After a return to a strong interest in color theory and Neo-Impressionism in 1895, he settled into a modified impressionist style for the rest of his life.

Hayet rarely exhibited in his lifetime, and has not always been included in more recent exhibitions. He showed with the Indépendants only once, in 1889, with Les XX in 1890, at Le Barc de Boutteville in 1894, and then held a succession of one-man shows in stores he himself rented for the purpose, twice in 1902, once in 1903, and once in 1904.

Among important works not in the present exhibition are *Camille and Lucien Pissarro Painting on the Banks of the Oise*, 1883 (watercolor, Private collection, Paris); *In the Café*, 1889 (encaustic, Private collection, Paris); *Place de la Concorde*, 1889 (encaustic, Wildenstein & Co.); *The Horse Stalls in the 1889 Exposition* (watercolor, Private collection, Paris); *Paris Landscape*, c. 1889–1890 (encaustic, W. J. Holliday, Indianapolis); *Landscape*, 1889 (encaustic, Ashmolean Museum, Oxford).

Bibliography: See BIBLIOGRAPHY 1, 15, 23, 29, and Jean Sutter, "Louis Hayet" in BIBLIOGRAPHY 2; F. Fagus, "Louis Hayet", *La Revue Blanche*, vol. 29, 1903, p. 619; W. S. Meadmore, *Lucien Pissarro*, London, 1962; Camille Pissarro (J. Rewald, ed.), *Lettres à son Fils Lucien*, Paris, 1950; Charles Saunier, "Louis Hayet", *La Revue Blanche*, vol. 27, 1902, p. 621, and "Hayet, Peintre inconnu", *Beaux-Arts*, 12 January 1934, p. 8; [Paul Signac] Anonymous, "Catalogue de l'Exposition des XX, Bruxelles", *Art et Critique*, 1 February 1890, p. 77.

"Hayet list" in the individual picture entries refers to the manuscript catalogue being prepared by J. Sutter.

31
THE CONCERT. 1886–1887.
Encaustic on paper over cardboard, 7 1/2 × 10 5/8″
(19 × 27 cm.).
Hayet list 95.

Early exhibition: Paris, 19 rue Lamartine, 19–30 November
1903.

Private collection, Paris.

A date close to 1886 is suggested by the fact that despite
the choppy brushwork, the colors are not truly divided. They
are instead local colors in concept, although perhaps the
blue and red-brown of the musician in the lower left corner
can be considered subdued color opposites.

32
PARIS, THE SHOPPING ARCADE (VUE DE PARIS,
LE PASSAGE). c. 1889.
Watercolor on calico, 7 1/8 × 9″ (18 × 23 cm.).
Hayet list 2.

Private collection, Paris.

33
DOORWAYS (LES PORTES). c. 1889.
Watercolor on muslin, 7 1/8 × 4 1/4" (18 × 11 cm.).
Hayet list 20.

Private collection, Paris.

Hayet invented a method of painting with watercolor,
gouache or encaustic on thin cloth, undoubtedly to take
advantage of the shimmer of light which will pass through
from the rear. As a painter-decorator, and familiar with the
theater, he might have been inspired by painted scenery in
which, since the time of the dioramas, different effects could
be had merely by changing the emphasis of the stage
lighting from the front to the rear of the backdrops. Here the
color red has been eliminated, and one therefore deduces
that behind the muslin Hayet placed backgrounds of solid
primary hues which would show through the weave of the
thin material. For instance, if the absent red is placed behind
Doorways, it turns the yellows and yellow oranges into
strong oranges, and the blue-violets into strong purples,
thereby creating the effect of late afternoon sunlight. If blue
is used, it produces the effect of indirect, cool light. Yellow
evokes an almost Sahara-like heat. Since the background
color is seen only in the interstices of the weave, it simulates
the effect of dotted brushwork.

There is no evidence that Hayet actually used such devices,
but no other explanation seems to suit the circumstances of
these paintings on cloth, and the particular color harmonies
that he used. Moreover, it would seem to agree with his
interest in particular effects of light, for in 1889 and 1890 he
exhibited pictures labeled "Sunlight", "Afternoon, sunshine",
"Morning, sunshine" and so forth.

Doorways is close in composition to the enigmatic drawing
of the same title by Seurat, in the Guggenheim Museum
collection.

34

PARIS, THE TREE-LINED AVENUE (SCENE DE PARIS).
1889.
Encaustic on paper over cardboard, 7 1/2 × 10 5/8"
(19 × 27 cm.).
Signed and dated recto l.r. "L.H. 89" and verso "L. Hayet 89".
Hayet list 115.

Private collection, Paris.

35
VEGETABLE MARKET (LE MARCHE). 1889.
Encaustic on paper over canvas, 7 1/4 × 10 1/2" (18.5 ×
26.5 cm.).
Signed and dated l.r. "L. Hayet 89".
Hayet list 121.

Collection Mr. and Mrs. Arthur G. Altschul, New York.

Hayet developed his own encaustic, in which he mixed
colors with some substance which has yet to be identified.
Like Seurat, Hayet wanted a surface free from changes
wrought by time, without the discoloration and other bad
effects of varnish. Seurat put his oils under glass, but Hayet
used a vehicle which needed no further protection, and
which has a characteristically matte appearance.

While the palette is quite his own, the composition is close
to Camille Pissarro, who made the open-air market into one
of his favored motifs [see no. 49].

Achille Laugé
(1861–1944)

Laugé was born in Arzens, in the Aude, on April 29, 1861, and lived until June 2, 1944. He was a follower of Neo-Impressionism rather than a member of the group in Paris. The son of well-to-do farmers (who moved to Cailhau, near Carcassonne, where Laugé spent most of his life), Laugé studied in Toulouse and then went to Paris in 1881. At the Ecole des Beaux-Arts in the capital, where he took instruction from Cabanel and J. P. Laurens, he met Aristide Maillol. Antoine Bourdelle, whom Laugé had known in Toulouse, joined them and the three maintained a long friendship. In 1888, after seven years in Paris (including a term of military service), Laugé returned south and established himself at Carcassonne for a few years. He returned to Cailhau in 1895 and spent the rest of his life there. Laugé's partisans would have it that he developed independently of Neo-Impressionism, but his pictures show otherwise. Since he was living in Paris in the critical years of 1886–1888, exhibited at the Indépendants in 1894, and travelled often to the capital, his contact with Neo-Impressionism is not to be wondered at. His best work is in the period 1900–1905, when his precise brushwork and divided color harmonized perfectly with his taut compositions.

Laugé has not been included in exhibitions of Neo-Impressionism, but he has been given a number of one-man shows since 1907. Before then, he showed with the Indépendants in 1894 and with the Nabis in Toulouse the same year. In 1907, Achille Astre exhibited his work in Paris, and the eminent critic Gustave Geffroy wrote a preface for the catalogue. Thereafter he was given exhibitions by Alvin-Beaumount in 1911, Nunès et Fiquet in 1919, Bernheim-Jeune in 1923, organizations in Toulouse and Perpignan in 1926, Georges Petit in 1927, Galerie de la Renaissance in 1929, René Zivy in 1930, the Musée de Limoux in 1958, the Musée des Augustins of Toulouse in 1961 [with Bourdelle and Maillol], Marcel Flavian in 1966, Kaplan Gallery of London also in 1966, and Hammer Galleries of New York in 1967.

Important paintings by Laugé include *Portrait of Mme. Astre*, 1892 (Musée de Carcassonne); *Landscape at La Gardie*, 1902 (Musée National d'Art Moderne, Paris); and *La Route en Automne*, c. 1902–1904 (Samuel Josefowitz, Switzerland).

Bibliography: The principal source is the catalogue by Charles Pornon of the exhibition *Achille Laugé et ses amis Bourdelle et Maillol*, Toulouse, 1961, and Gustave Geffroy's prefaces for the exhibitions at Achille Astre in 1907 and Nunès et Fiquet in 1919.

36
L'HORT A CAILHAU. c. 1905.
Oil on canvas, 37 3/8 × 45 1/4" (95 × 115 cm.).
Signed l.r. "A. Laugé".

Early exhibition: Perhaps Paris, Indépendants, 20 March – 30 April 1906, no. 2820 ("Route de Caillau") [sic].

Collection Musée Fabre, Montpellier.

67

Henri Le Sidaner

(1862–1939)

Le Sidaner was a conservative artist who adapted Neo-Impressionism to his own purposes, beginning about 1898. He is therefore a "petit maître" and follower of Neo-Impressionism like Henri Martin and many others, but his work has substantial quality. He came to Paris in 1880 and studied with Cabanel for two years, then moved to Etaples near Boulogne for the next twelve years. Upon his return to Paris in 1894, he absorbed the fin-de-siècle fondness for twilight scenes, which became his veritable specialty. One senses Eugène Carrière and Whistler in his work, and by about 1900, Le Sidaner was the French counterpart to the Italian *Divisionisti* like Grubicy de Dragon and Pelizza [no. 163], although there was probably no direct relationship. His painting below is typical of Le Sidaner at his best. Color is divided along Neo-Impressionist lines. The green and pink tablecloth is one opposition; another is the yellow and purple of the walls of the house, but the purple is rather dull, and the greys and drab greens further mute the contrasts.

Camille Mauclair wrote the principal study of Le Sidaner in 1928, and his major retrospective was at the Palais Galliéra in Paris in 1948.

37
THE TABLE IN THE GARDEN (LA TABLE AU JARDIN).
c. 1904.
Oil on canvas, 35 1/2 × 46" (90 × 117 cm.).
Signed l.l. "Le Sidaner".

Collection Musée des Beaux-Arts, Ghent.

Maximilian Luce
(1858–1941)

Artisan, engraver and graphic artist, illustrator, painter, and political activist, Luce had one of the richest and most varied lives of the Neo-Impressionists. Without sharing Signac's role as effective leader of the group, he had an even wider circle of friends, and his life history is interlocked particularly with Angrand, Gausson, the Pissarros, Signac and Van Rysselberghe. The son of a poor clerk, Luce was apprenticed to the wood engraver Hildebrand by the age of fourteen. Four years later he went to work for Eugène Froment, whose shop produced woodcuts for *L'Illustration*, the *Graphic* of London (Luce worked there for two months in 1877), and countless other journals. It was there that he met Léo Gausson and, with Cavallo-Peduzzi, they formed the "Lagny group". Cavallo was enrolled at the Ecole des Beaux-Arts, but Luce followed an irregular series of classes with several artists, including the famous Carolus-Duran. In November, 1879, the same month that Seurat left the Ecole for military service at Brest, Luce was conscripted. However, after eighteen months of service away from Paris (during which he continued to draw and paint), Luce was permitted to return and adopt his customary life, although he was subject to military orders until 1883. Carolus-Duran had a hand in this partial release from service, and Luce continued to work with him off and on until 1885. He was meantime employed at Froment's and Auguste Lançon's although this work dropped off suddenly in 1883 when the new zinc lithography began replacing the traditional techniques. Often sharing quarters with Cavallo and Gausson, both at Lagny and in Paris, Luce became more of a full-time painter. By 1887 he had met Seurat, Signac, the Pissarros, and the other Neo-Impressionists, and he exhibited at the Indépendants for the first time. His paintings of that year are in the divided color and stippled textures of Neo-Impressionism, and he was treated as a leading member of the group from that time onwards. He showed with the Indépendants every year, and with Les XX in 1889 and 1892.

Like most of the Neo-Impressionists, Luce was an Anarchist-Communist, and was a friend of Jean Grave, Emile Pouget, Jules Vallès and the Belgian Elisée Reclus. He contributed innumerable illustrations to the whole gamut of Anarchist publications, and was imprisoned in 1894. From late 1895 to the end of the century he travelled and painted frequently in the infamous "Black Country" of Belgium (where Van Gogh had lived years earlier), especially at Charleroi and the Sambre valley. Toward the end of the decade he began turning away from Neo-Impressionism and gradually adopted a manner closer to that of earlier Impressionism. His political activity waned after the turn of the century, and he spent the rest of his productive life in painting and drawing.

Luce has appeared in all group exhibitions of Neo-Impressionism, and has been given a number of one-man shows: *La Revue Indépendante* in 1888; Petite Revue Documentaire, in 1895; Durand-Ruel in 1899 and 1922; Druet in 1904, 1906, and 1926; Bernheim-Jeune in 1907, 1909, 1910, 1914, 1916, and 1929; Choiseul in 1914; Flechtheim (Düsseldorf) also in 1914; Galerie Marseille in 1920 and 1952; Galerie Dru in 1921 and 1930; Galerie d'Art de Montparnasse in 1928; Berri-Raspail in 1941; Indépendants in 1942; l'Elysée in 1948; Lorenceau the same year; Wildenstein (London) in 1954; Maison de la Pensée Française, 1958; Musée Municipal de Saint-Denis, also 1958; Henri Bénézit, 1959; Charleroi, 1966.

Important paintings not in this exhibition include *The Artist's Room*, c. 1878 (Frédéric Luce, Paris); *The Ragpicker*, 1887 (Private collection, Paris); *Le Pont Neuf, Evening*, 1889 (Art market, New York); *The Seine at Herblay*, 1892 (Art market, Paris); *The Thames at London*, 1893 (Private collection, Lausanne); *La Rue des Abbesses, l'Epicerie*, 1896 (Oscar Ghez, Geneva); *The Cathedral of Gisors*, 1898 (Private collection, Paris); *Factory Chimneys*, 1898–1899 (Private collection, Paris); *The Seine*, 1899 (Count Doria, Paris); *Notre-Dame*, c. 1900–1904 (Jean Matisse, Pontoise).

Bibliography: See BIBLIOGRAPHY 1, 5, 8, 9, 15, 20, 22, 23, 24, 26, 27, 28, 29 and Jean Sutter, "Maximilien Luce" in BIBLIOGRAPHY 2; Anonymous, "Exposition Maximilien Luce", *L'Art Moderne*, vol. 15, no. 44, 3 November 1895, p. 349; Jules Christophe, "Maximilien Luce", *Les Hommes d'Aujourd'hui*, 1890; Félix Fénéon, preface to the exhibition at Druet, 1904; Camille Pissarro (J. Rewald, ed.), *Lettres à son Fils Lucien*, Paris, 1950; Robert Rousseau (ed.), *Maximilien Luce*, catalogue of exhibition at Charleroi, 1966 [chronologies by J. Sutter]; A. Tabarant, *Maximilien Luce*, Paris, 1928; Emile Verhaeren, preface to the exhibition at Bernheim-Jeune, 1909.

38

OUTSKIRTS OF MONTMARTRE (TERRAINS A MONT-
MARTRE). 1887.
Oil on canvas, 18 × 32″ (45.5 × 81 cm.).
Signed and dated l.r. "Luce 87".

Early exhibition: Probably Paris, Indépendants, 22 March –
3 April 1888, no. 437 ("Terrain, rue Championnet");
Brussels, Les XX, February 1889, no. 6 ("Terrains à
Montmartre").

Formerly Camille Pissarro.
Collection Rijksmuseum Kröller-Müller, Otterlo.

Montmartre, as we know it today, was built largely in the last
decades of the nineteenth century, and Luce lived there on the
rue Cortot at the time this picture was first exhibited. The
Impressionists had paid surprisingly little attention to the
extensive rebuilding of Paris which took place beginning in
the 1850s, and preferred landscape and village sites outside
the capital. The Neo-Impressionists, however, incorporated
the city, especially its most ordinary aspects, into their
concept of modernity. Luce frequently showed scenes of
streets and houses under construction, and Signac and
Seurat painted the homely new suburbs and factories of

Clichy, Asnières and Courbevoie. Since they were all
partisans of the Anarchist-Communist movement, the city
street appears in their art as a logical expression of a concern
for the realities of contemporary society.

39

THE KITCHEN (UNE CUISINE). 1888–1889.
Oil on canvas, 25 1/2 × 21 1/8" (64.8 × 53.7 cm.).
Signed l.r. "Luce".

Early exhibition: Paris, Indépendants, 20 March – 17 April
1890, no. 501.

Private collection, Paris.

Seurat and Signac each did several monumental interiors in the
1880s, but otherwise Neo-Impressionism is a style of
landscape painting. Luce also favored landscape, but
nonetheless painted more interiors than any of his friends.
Here the strong play of light and dark, within a conventional
spatial structure derived from the Dutch, provides a classic
lesson in Neo-Impressionist color. In the lower left corner,
the floor would be all the same color "in reality", but the
contrast between light and shade produces two different
effects. The lighter portion has blues and greens dominating
and tending to show in our vision as a blue-green. In the
adjacent shadow, all hues are darker in value, and they are
also more intense because they are not overlaid with the
bleach-like film of sunlight. The reds and blues dominate but
since they are seen separately, they attain the characteristic
vibration the painters sought. Throughout the picture, Luce
increases the contrasts of hue and value as two areas meet,
creating zonal bands that look forward to Analytical Cubism
of 1911.

41

LA RUE MOUFFETARD. 1889–1890.
Oil on canvas, 31 1/2 × 25 1/2" (80 × 64.8 cm.).
Signed l.r. "Luce".

Early exhibition: Paris, Indépendants, 20 March – 27 April
1890, no. 493.

Lent by Hammer Galleries of New York.

This and the previous picture were painted from the same
spot in south-central Paris. The building to the left of the
church is the one which dominates the right side of *La Rue
Mouffetard*. It was then, as today, a working-class and
market district, perfectly suited to Luce's wish to paint all
aspects of the life of the urban poor. Close by were the
offices of *La Révolte*, the Anarchist review to which Luce
and the Neo-Impressionists were contributors and whose
editor, Jean Grave, was their friend. The church in the
previous painting is seen in the strong light of mid-afternoon.
Its horizontal framing lets the strong greens of the square's
foliage bring a feeling of country landscape into the city.
The other picture is of vertical format to stress the way the
flanking buildings form a canyon of the street. It is later in
the afternoon, and most of the picture is in indirect light,
which causes the blues to take on greater prominence. The

unmixed combination of blue and pink in both sky and
pavement is a curious harmony found only in Luce, and the
patches of intense green in the foreground are also typical of
his palette. At the same time, relationships with other Neo-
Impressionists are readily observed: the sun strikes the tops
of the buildings as it does in Lucien Pissarro's street scene
[no. 60], and the street market is a subject favored by the
elder Pissarro and by Hayet [nos. 49 and 35].

40
L'EGLISE SAINT-MEDARD. 1889–1890.
Oil on canvas, 25 3/4 × 32″ (65.4 × 81 cm.).
Signed l.l. "Luce".

Early exhibition: Paris, Indépendants, 20 March – 27 April
1890, no. 494.

Formerly Frédéric Luce; Petrignani.
Collection B. E. Bensinger, Chicago

42

LA SEINE A HERBLAY. 1890.
Oil on canvas, 19 5/8 × 31 1/8″ (50 × 79 cm.).
Signed and dated l.r. "Luce 90".

Early exhibition: Probably Paris, Indépendants, 20 March –
27 April 1891, no. 791.

Collection Musée National d'Art Moderne, Paris.

Camille Pissarro was, indirectly, Luce's teacher in the two
city views. Signac was Luce's host at Herblay in 1890 and,
though younger, he seems to have transmitted to Luce
something of his hotter palette and his love of river basins
and seaports. In the foreground, the bright sun strikes the
autumn foliage to create relatively autonomous zones, each
devoted to one portion of the spectrum: reds, oranges and
pinks in one band, next to another controlled by green. In the
middleground, however, each zone develops its own internal
contrasts. Along the river, left of center, there are blues
mixed with the reds and oranges.

43
QUAY AT CAMARET, FINISTERE. 1894.
Oil on canvas, 35 × 46″ (88.9 × 116.8 cm.).
Signed and dated l.r. "Luce 94".

Early exhibition: Probably Brussels, La Libre Esthétique,
February 1895, no. 383 ("Le Port de Camaret, crépuscule").

Formerly Félix Fénéon.
Collection Museum of Fine Arts, Springfield, Massachusetts,
James Philip Gray Collection.

44
LA RUE DES ABBESSES, PARIS. 1896.
Charcoal, 8 3/8 × 12 3/8″ (21.4 × 31.4 cm.).
Signed l.l. "Rue des Abbesses Luce".

Collection Mr. and Mrs. Hugo Perls, New York.

One of several drawings for the painting of 1896 now in the
collection of Oscar Ghez, Geneva.

45

NOTRE-DAME. 1900–1901.
Oil on canvas, 33 1/2 × 31 1/4" (85 × 79.4 cm.).
Signed and dated l.l. "Luce 1900–1901".

Formerly Frédéric Luce.
Collection Mr. and Mrs. Arthur G. Altschul, New York.

Many of Luce's paintings by 1900 were in a smoother
brushstroke and undivided color, but he continued his Neo-
Impressionist style in certain pictures, notably in those
where the human figure is absent or in small scale. His wish
to have brushwork correspond to his conception of human
form was one reason for abandoning the stippled textures.
Luce painted Notre-Dame several times at the turn of the
century, and Matisse's later views of the famous monument
might have something to do with his. Jean Matisse owns
today a painting by Luce of Notre-Dame which was done
about 1903–1905 from the window of Henri Matisse's studio
on the sixth floor of 19 Quai Saint-Michel. Earlier this had
been Dubois-Pillet's address. Matisse's Luce is a sketch in
large dabs, but the present composition is a highly polished
exercise, a careful adjustment of value that makes it one of
Luce's finest in his last Neo-Impressionist phase.

Hippolyte Petitjean
(1854–1929)

Petitjean was born at Mâcon on September 11, 1854 and died exactly 75 years later, September 17, 1929. He was more a follower of Neo-Impressionism than a participant, but he appeared in exhibitions with the Neo-Impressionists from 1892 onwards. After training in Mâcon, Petitjean came to Paris in 1872 and entered Cabanel's studio. He continued on the side his trade as painter-decorator for some time, rather like Hayet. His very conservative style, based upon an admiration for Puvis de Chavannes, won him official Salon honors in 1888 and again later, but gradually he adopted the Neo-Impressionist manner. Beginning in 1891 he exhibited regularly with the Indépendants and in 1892 in the little gallery exhibitions devoted to the Neo-Impressionists; he showed also with Les XX in Brussels in 1893 and with La Libre Esthétique there in 1898. His period of greatest proximity to Neo-Impressionism was from about 1890 to 1894. Thereafter his many compositions of bathers of vaguely mythological ambiance retain a superficial use of small brushstrokes, but without divided color. They are often very close to Puvis de Chavannes and to Fantin-Latour. About 1912, perhaps realizing that his work had lost decisive quality, Petitjean returned to the Neo-Impressionists palette and produced a great many watercolors and a few oils, of which the best are pure landscapes. With their characteristic round dots, rather widely spaced and showing white paper between, his watercolors of the late period are easily recognized and it is all the more wonder that unwary collectors have accepted the many forged dates of the 1880s which have been added in recent years. Petitjean's finest works are his drawings in black and white of the years 1895 to about 1905.

Aside from the exhibitions mentioned above, Petitjean has had one-man exhibitions at the Galerie de l'Institut in 1966 and Findlay Galleries in New York in 1959.

Some of his more interesting paintings are the *Portrait of the Artist's Wife*, 1892 (Musée d'Art Moderne, Paris); *Mythological Scene*, 1895 (Walter P. Chrysler, Jr., New York); *Gathering Flowers*, 1913 (Oscar Ghez, Geneva); *Landscape at Donzy-le-Perthuis*, 1916 (Inspection des Musées de Province, Paris).

Bibliography: See BIBLIOGRAPHY 1, 23, 29, and Lily Bazalgette, "Hippolyte Petitjean" in BIBLIOGRAPHY 2; Tristan Klingsor [i.e., Leclère] "Hippolyte Petitjean", *Art et Artiste*, vol. 19, January 1930, pp. 138–139; Camille Pissarro (J. Rewald, ed.), *Lettres à son fils Lucien*, Paris, 1950.

46
THE WASH-HOUSE (LAVOIR A ANTONY, BORD DE LA BIEVRE). 1891–1892?
Oil on canvas, 8 1/2 × 12 5/8″ (21.5 × 32 cm.).
Stamped l.r. "Atelier Hipp. Petitjean" and also verso on stretcher.

Formerly Mlle. Marcelle Petitjean.
Private collection, Paris.

The tender palette and the soft dabs suggest a date early in Petitjean's evolution towards Neo-Impressionism, and this might well be the years 1887–1888 as tradition has it. However, a date closer to 1891–1892, when Petitjean first began exhibiting with the Neo-Impressionists, seems more likely.

47
VILLAGE. 1893.
Oil on canvas, 23 3/4 × 15" (60.4 × 38 cm.).
Signed and dated l.l. "hipp. Petitjean 93".

Lent by Roland, Browse & Delbanco, London.

The classic Neo-Impressionist palette is found here in a very
pretty balance, with pinks, blues and yellows for the sky,
blues, reds and violets for the dark areas, and orange over
blue for the lighter planes of the buildings. The innate
tendency of Neo-Impressionism as a group style was
towards a simplified surface pattern, emphasized by the
modular brushwork. This picture carries the style toward
Cubism, and its central portion and the subject foretell the
structure of such a picture as Braque's *Céret: the Rooftops*
[no. 169], although it would be wrong to posit any direct
relationship.

Camille Pissarro
(1830–1903)

The threads of Neo-Impressionism are woven into Pissarro's oeuvre for nearly a decade. In the years just before 1886, his work formed one of the chief inspirations for Seurat; it then merged with the new current so that the elder artist became a prominent figure in the movement for four years; the year 1890 was a time of transition in which divided color was observed, but with decreasing use of opposed colors and a gradual loosening of the brushwork; 1891 marked the end of Pissarro's Neo-Impressionism, although its presence is felt in his paintings for another two years. This long phase is largely suppressed in studies of Pissarro, and critics have borrowed from the artist's own disavowal of Neo-Impressionism in the 1890s to condemn the work of the late 1880s. He was, however, a fully fledged participant and maintained great enthusiasm from early 1886 at least until the summer of 1888. In the early 1880s, long established as one of the leading Impressionists, Pissarro began to tighten his chopped-straw brushwork more than before, in some cases going so far as to give the same texture to his figures' costumes, flesh and to the landscape. At the same time, he clarified his compositions by reducing the number of different planes and by articulating them clearly, and he began to treat the human figure in large scale. In these several ways, Pissarro helped prepare the way for Neo-Impressionism, as Seurat himself later acknowledged. He met Seurat in October, 1885, and his instant conversion (even before Signac) to the young artist's ideas was only possible because they struck the elder painter as the logical next step to take. He brought Seurat, Signac and his son Lucien into the last Impressionist exhibition in May, and referred to himself as a "scientific Impressionist", while his former comrades were called "romantic Impressionists". He was invigorated by the younger society, and dined often with Signac, Dubois-Pillet, Luce and others, also joining in evenings with the young Symbolist writers. To give his son his own niche, Camille did not exhibit with the Indépendants, although he did show at Les XX in Brussels in 1887, 1889 and 1891.

From the autumn of 1888, Pissarro began to complain that the Neo-Impressionist technique hampered the spontaneity he wished to return to. He slowly modified the rigor of the small brushstrokes, and allowed the local colors to dominate the contrasts more often, but he continued to observe the division of color until well into 1891. However, it seems best to limit Pissarro's Neo-Impressionist period to the years 1886–1890, and regard 1891 as a transitional year. The fine hatchwork of color which reappeared to the end of his life is one of the legacies of his work of the later 1880s. So, too, perhaps, is the fact that he turned to Paris for his subject matter in the 1890s for the first time, because if we must grant Corot and Monet a priority, it was particularly Luce, Dubois-Pillet, Angrand, Hayet, Seurat and Signac on occasions, and his son Lucien, who gave Paris streets and quays a major place in the 1880s, when the older Impressionists had forsaken it.

Pissarro's many one-man exhibitions, too numerous to list, began in 1883 at Durand-Ruel; the most recent was in 1965, at Wildenstein & Co., New York. Chief among his Neo-Impressionist paintings are *The Railway to Dieppe*, 1886 (Pissarro-Venturi 694; Private collection, Gladwyne, Pa.); *Woman in an Orchard*, 1887 (Pissarro-Venturi 709; Louvre); *Peasant Houses, Eragny*, 1887 (Pissarro-Venturi 710; National Art Gallery of New South Wales, Sydney); *Ile Lacroix, Rouen, effect of Fog*, 1888 (Pissarro-Venturi 719; John G. Johnson Collection, Philadelphia); *Peasants in the Fields, Eragny*, 1890 (Pissarro-Venturi 755; Albright-Knox Art Gallery, Buffalo).

Bibliography: See BIBLIOGRAPHY 1, 5, 6, 8, 9, 22, 23, 24, 26, 27, 29, and Ludovic Rodo Pissarro and Lionello Venturi, *Camille Pissarro, son, art, son œuvre* [catalogue raisonné], Paris, 1939; Loÿs Delteil, *Pissarro, Sisley, Renoir* [catalogue of graphic work, vol. 17 of *Le peintre-graveur illustré*], Paris, 1923; Camille Pissarro (J. Rewald, ed.), *Lettres à son fils Lucien*, Paris, 1950; John Rewald, *Camille Pissarro*, New York, 1963, and *The History of Impressionism*, Museum of Modern Art, 1946 *et seq.;* A. Tabarant, *Pissarro*, Paris, 1924 and New York, 1925; Lionello Venturi (ed.), *Les Archives de l'Impressionnisme*, 2 vols, Paris, 1939.

48

LE COURS-LA-REINE, ROUEN. 1883.
Oil on canvas, 21 1/2 × 25 1/2″ (54.6 × 64.8 cm.).
Signed and dated l.l. "C. Pissarro 1883".
Pissarro-Venturi catalogue 603.

Early exhibition: New York, Durand-Ruel, 23 November –
7 December 1912, no. 3.

Collection Mr. and Mrs. Paul M. Hirschland, New York.

This is not a Neo-Impressionist work, but demonstrates how
Pissarro foretold the later style in his tightly laced brushwork
that is close to the technique Seurat used in 1884–1885
[no. 76]. It is Jongkind who first used such a choppy surface
in similar compositions and subjects of the 1860s.

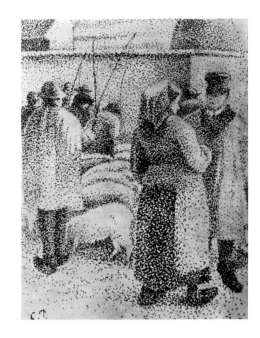

49

THE PIG MARKET (MARCHE DES COCHONS, SAINT-
MARTIN). 1886.
Ink, 6 5/8 × 5″ (16.8 × 12.7 cm.).
Signed l.l. "C.P.".

Formerly Lucien Pissarro; Mr. and Mrs. John Rewald.
Collection Max Kaganovitch, Paris.

"I have done two ink drawings in dots", Camille wrote his
son on December 27, 1886 [*Lettres*, see above], "a *Petit
Marché* and a *St. Martin* (pig dealers). They came out not
badly. Now if I could get them published in a review, that
would bring in a few sous [. . .]. Mounted, these drawings
look very well [. . .]. The dot is still capable of frightening
our charming bourgeois!". Three days later he wrote of a
third drawing in the same technique (the *Petit Marché* he
mentions is now in the Lehman Collection). It was logical
to think of them for publication, because the uniform
blackness of each little stroke can be reproduced with slight
loss, unlike subtle grey tones of traditional technique.
Besides, there would be an automatic association with the
graphic arts, for the fine strokes recall the grain of the
aquatint process and the tiny dots of the older stipple
engraving. Nonetheless, although he was a skilled print-
maker, Pissarro used the dotted manner only in a few ink
drawings, never in prints.

Dotted ink drawings, which echoed the textures of Neo-
Impressionist oil paintings, were a veritable fad from the
middle of 1886 until 1888, and many of them were
reproduced in contemporary journals. Signac [no. 91] and
Dubois-Pillet [no. 25] were especially fond of them, and
Van Gogh used dotted textures in many of his drawings.

50

SPRINGTIME IN ERAGNY (PRINTEMPS A ERAGNY). 1886.
Oil on canvas, 21 1/4 × 26″ (54 × 66 cm.).
Signed and dated l.l. "C. Pissarro 1886".
Pissarro-Venturi catalogue 693.

Collection Mr. and Mrs. Hugo Dixon, Memphis, Tennessee.

According to Seurat himself, Pissarro was the first to convert
to the Neo Impressionist technique, even before Signac. In
January or February, 1886, Pissarro exhibited a little Neo-
Impressionist picture in a dealer's window, the first such
picture ever shown, since Seurat did not exhibit his Neo-
Impressionist works until May.

This painting was done in the spring of 1886, on the eve of
the last Impressionist exhibition, in which Pissarro, his son,
Seurat and Signac showed their works together in a separate
room. Pissarro has adopted more the manner than the
substance of Neo-Impressionism. Color is not truly divided,
but is put down in variations of the local color with only a
sprinkling of contrasting hues. The dabs are rather widely
spaced and lie on the surface, not yet forming a dense
interweave, in this way resembling the work of Lucien
[no. 55] and Gausson [no. 29] of the same year.

51
LANDSCAPE AT ERAGNY (PAYSAGE D'ERAGNY).   85
1886–1887.
Watercolor, 4 7/8 × 8″ (12.5 × 20.3 cm.).
Stamped l.l. ''C.P.''.

Formerly Paulemile Pissarro; Mr. and Mrs. John Rewald.
Lent by Jacques O'Hana, London.

52

APPLE HARVEST AT ERAGNY (LA CUEILLETTE DES
POMMES, ERAGNY). 1888.
Oil on canvas, 23 5/8 × 28 3/4" (60 × 73 cm.).
Signed and dated l.r. "C. Pissarro 1888".
Pissarro-Venturi catalogue 726.

Early exhibitions: Brussels, Les XX, February 1889, no. 5
(dated 1887 by mistake); Paris, Boussod-Valadon, February
1890, no. 6.

Formerly Victor Desfossés; Dr. Max Emden; Max Epstein.
Collection Dallas Museum of Fine Arts, Munger Fund.

The extraordinary shadow of the tree already has a feeling of
the Art Nouveau, and in particular looks forward to the two
farm scenes of 1893 by Cross [nos. 15, 16]. Van Gogh
comes to mind in the blocky drawing of the figures, so does
Millet who was the principal master of the human form for
both painters (and Pissarro had visited the large Millet
retrospective in Paris in 1887). The quality of his own art
which he had long called "savage" and "primitive" is one
which Pissarro associated with the clear order of Neo-
Impressionism. "Disorder", he said of Monet's pictures
[January 9, 1887, to Lucien, in *Lettres*, see above], "comes

out of this romantic fantasy which, despite the artist's talent,
is not in harmony with our epoch". "Understand", he wrote
in the same letter, "we will yet have with us all the people
who are not haunted by romanticism, who have instead the
idea of nature that is simple, naïve, like the primitives, which
does not exclude character nor science".

The color of this painting is no longer that of 1886 [no. 50].
Already in 1887 he had added strong contrasts to his palette,
and here they are brought to a climax. Compared, for
example, with an early apple harvest of 1881 [Pissarro-
Venturi 545; Mr. and Mrs. William B. Jaffe, New York], these
differences are found in the tree shadows: The early picture
has several closely related colors—blues, violets, greenish-
yellows—which produce an effect of a greyish blue. The
nearest thing to color opposites, yellows and violets, were
scumbled together when wet, leading to a rather grey result.
In the Neo-Impressionist picture, the shadow has brilliant red,
intense blue, intense green, as well as pink, lavender, orange,
some yellow, and subdued blues and greens. The pigments
were not allowed to mix much together, and preserve their
individuality which, because of the high intensity, results in
an abrasive vibration in our eye that cannot be resolved into

one tone. In order to make the contrast still sharper, Pissarro strengthens the blue around the edges of the shadow, a reaction provoked by the proximity of the strong sunlit field.

VIEW FROM THE ARTIST'S WINDOW, ERAGNY (VUE DE MA FENETRE, ERAGNY). 1888.

Oil on canvas, 25 5/8 × 31 7/8" (65 × 81 cm.).
Signed and dated I.I. "C. Pissarro 1888".
Pissarro-Venturi catalogue 721.

Early exhibition: Paris, Durand-Ruel, "Peintres-graveurs", January—February 1889.

Formerly Lucien Pissarro.
Collection The Visitors of the Ashmolean Museum, Oxford.

The more even light and softer harmonies are closer than the previous picture to Pissarro's earlier paintings, but it is an equally thorough embodiment of Neo-Impressionist principles. Its palette is rather close to Seurat's at the time of the *Grande Jatte* [nos. 74, 75, 76]. The principle opposition of green and red is fortified by such devices as the intensification of green next to the red roof in the center, to form a contrast-halo.

54

OLD CHELSEA BRIDGE, LONDON (PONT EN CON-
STRUCTION A CHELSEA, LONDRES). 1890.
Oil on canvas, 23 1/2 × 28 1/2" (59.7 × 72.4 cm.).
Signed and dated l.l. "C. Pissarro 1890".

Early exhibition: Brussels, Les XX, February 1891, no. 1
("Pont en construction à Chelsea, Londres").

Formerly W. van Horne.
Private collection, New York.

Pissarro visited London in the spring of 1890, with
Maximilien Luce and his son Lucien, who settled there
permanently at the end of the year. He had been there in
1870–1871, and returned again in 1892 (also with Luce) and
in 1897. The motif of the bridge, which he and Monet
favored all their lives, is rendered here in a criss-cross
brushwork resembling his work before 1886, but suiting still
the Neo-Impressionist concept of divided color. The orange-
red over the blues of the bridge is an opposition of hue much
favored by Seurat.

London, particularly the Thames and its bridges, was of great
importance to French painting at the end of the century and
represented a return to the homeland of Constable and
Turner, who had helped set French landscape along the path
towards Impressionism many years earlier. Monet had been
in London during the Franco-Prussian war, and in 1899
began a whole series of pictures there. In addition to the
Pissarros and Luce, Hayet, Signac, Finch and Lemmen
[no. 130] painted there in the 1890s, and Derain's Neo-
Impressionist pictures include several of London.

Lucien Pissarro
(1863–1944)

Lucien was the eldest son of Camille Pissarro, and was trained entirely by his father. The large family was always in need as Lucien grew up, but his father managed to support him until 1887, a dependency that was characteristic of his art, also. In 1883–1884, Lucien spent a year in London, studying on his own, then returned to Eragny, not far from Paris, where Camille had finally settled his family after years of moving about. Along with Seurat and Signac, he joined the last Impressionist exhibition in May, 1886, and that year also began to show regularly with the Indépendants. He spent the summer of 1886 with Signac, and was on intimate terms with Hayet, Luce, Dubois-Pillet, Gausson, the Belgian Théo Van Rysselberghe, and frequently saw Seurat, Angrand, and Van Gogh. In 1887 he began working for the publisher Manzi, and in addition produced a great many woodcuts and illustrations for a variety of reviews, including the anarchist press. His contributions to the Indépendants regularly included prints, drawings and various projects for illustrations. Daumier is felt strongly in his graphic work, as well as Millet, his own father and, beginning in mid-1887, Seurat also.

Hoping to find a market for his drawings and prints, and to give lessons in art, Lucien moved to London in November, 1890 (the Pissarro family had cousins there with whom they had maintained close contact). Perhaps he was already disillusioned with Neo-Impressionism but, in any event, he was soon caught up in the British arts and crafts movement (his cousin and wife, Esther Bensusan, was a Ruskin-Morris disciple) through his friendship with Charles Ricketts and Charles Shannon. He remained in England the rest of his life, occupying a very important role as intermediary between the artists in France and Belgium, and England. His painting gradually drew away from his father's style, but with the increase in personal flavor came a rather soft manner that is often only pretty. His many woodcuts and the illustrated books he produced on his own Eragny Press are his best work after the Neo-Impressionist period.

In addition to his exhibitions with the Indépendants from 1886 to 1894, Lucien showed at Brussels with Les XX and La Libre Esthétique in 1890, 1892, 1894, 1895 and 1896. He has been included in most exhibitions devoted to Neo-Impressionism, and was given a number of one-man shows, most of them in London: by Leigh in 1921, Leicester Galleries in 1922, 1924, 1943 [with Camille and Orovida Pissarro], 1946, 1947 and 1950, the Arts Council of Great Britain in 1952 and 1963, and O'Hana in 1954; also by Bernheim-Jeune in Paris, 1924 [with Le Mayeur] and 1934 [with Camille Pissarro], the Manchester City Art Gallery in 1935, the Belfast Museum and Art Gallery in 1936 and Lee Malone in New York, in 1964.

Some of his principal pictures of the Neo-Impressionist period are *Landscape, Eragny*, 1887 (formerly Paulémile Pissarro); *The Church at Gisors*, 1888 (Musée National d'Art Moderne, Paris); *Jeanne in the Garden at Eragny*, 1889 (Orovida Pissarro, Oxford); *Portrait of Jeanne*, 1889 (Orovida Pissarro).

Bibliography: See BIBLIOGRAPHY 1, 8, 9, 15, 22, 23, 26, 29, and W. S. Meadmore, *Lucien Pissarro*, London, 1962; Anonymous, "Lucien Pissarro", reprinted from *Gil Blas* in *L'Art Moderne*, vol. 13, no. 32, 6 August 1893, p. 255; T. S. Moore, *A Brief Account of the origin of the Eragny Press*, London, 1903; Camille Pissarro (J. Rewald, ed.), *Lettres à son fils Lucien*, Paris, 1950; Lucien Pissarro and Charles Ricketts, *De la Typographie et de l'Harmonie de la page Imprimée, William Morris et son influence* [. . .], Paris and London, 1898; Lucien Pissarro, *Rossetti* [Masterpieces in Color series], London and New York, 1908.

55

THE CHURCH AT ERAGNY (L'EGLISE D'ERAGNY). 1886.
Oil on canvas, 20 1/8 × 27 1/2" (51 × 70 cm.).
Signed and dated l.l. "Lucien Pissarro 1886".

Early exhibition: Probably Paris, Indépendants, 26 March –
3 May 1887, no. 369 ("Route de Gisors [app. à Mlle C.]").

Collection The Visitors of the Aohmolean Museum, Oxford.

The identical site was painted in 1884 by Lucien's father
Camille [Pissarro-Venturi 649], called *View of Eragny*. By
comparison, Lucien's shows the younger generation of Neo-
Impressionists at work. The horizon line is much higher,
creating more positive surface shapes out of the different
areas; the shadows are given strong identity as autonomous
shapes; the elimination of cows in the field and a man on the
roadway results in a starkness that suits the tauter geometry
of the whole composition. The division of color is not carried
as far as in Gausson's landscape of the same year [no. 29],
but the greens in the field are divided: blues multiplying in the
shaded areas, yellow-tans and pale oranges in the light.
Throughout the field, Lucien has placed dots of blue and
green exactly in the center of larger discs of the lighter
colors, a rather didactic creation of haloes of color opposites
which Seurat, too, used in his two studies of 1886–1887

[Louvre] for the lateral figures of his monumental *Models.* Lucien's picture has sometimes been given the date of 1887, but is clearly signed 1886. It was probably the painting shown with the Indépendants in 1887 as the *Route de Gisors,* for Gisors is only two miles from Eragny, and this title gives a better expression of the picture than the one it now bears.

56

WOMAN SEWING BY A WINDOW (FEMME COUSANT). 1886.

Gouache, 6 × 8″ (15.2 × 20.3 cm.).
Monogram and date l.l. "LP déc. 86".

Formerly Orovida Pissarro.
Collection Jacques O'Hana, London.

The choice of colors and the technique are very much like his friend Hayet's watercolors on cloth [nos. 32, 33]. *Woman Sewing* has frequently been exhibited as *The Artist's Wife,* but given the date, this is patently impossible. The subject is more likely his mother.

58

VILLAGE STREET BY THE RIVER. 1888.
Oil on canvas, 23 × 28″ (58.5 × 71 cm.).
Signed l.l. "Lucien Pissarro 1888".

Formerly Ludovic-Rodo Pissarro.
Collection Mr. and Mrs. Samuel Josefowitz, Switzerland.

The site is Gouvernes, to the east of Paris not far from Lagny,
in the Marne district favored by Luce and Gausson. Like the
previous picture, the composition and the type of subject
go back to Corot, by way of Lucien's father, whose view of
Osny of 1883 [Pissarro-Venturi 582] is the essential
prototype.

57

SPRING AT ERAGNY (PRINTEMPS A ERAGNY). 1888.   93
Oil on canvas, 23 3/4 × 28 3/4" (60.4 × 73 cm.).
Signed and dated l.r. "Lucien Pissarro 1888".

Collection Mr. and Mrs. Arthur G. Altschul, New York.

The saturated greens of this picture have little contrasting
colors with them for, like Camille, Lucien conceived still of
harmonies based upon similar hues. Several of his paintings
of the period are subtitled *temps gris* (grey, or cloudy
weather), since indirect light suited these less contrasted
harmonies. Camille painted the same fields, with young fruit
trees in their protective supports, in 1884, 1886 and 1887
[Pissarro-Venturi 642, 702, 709, 711].

59

THE GARDEN PATH. c. 1889.

Oil on canvas, 17 1/2 × 14 1/2" (44.5 × 37 cm.).

Monogram l.r. "LP".

Collection Mr. and Mrs. Morris Leverton, New York.

This picture could almost be a pendant for *Jeanne in the Garden at Eragny* of 1889, and that date might be posited anyway because of the closeness of the palette to paintings signed and dated 1889 by Louis Hayet, Lucien's friend. Moreover, the pigment does not seem to be the usual oils, and might well be a case of Lucien's using Hayet's encaustic recipe. The striking foreground is based upon the contrasts of the yellow-cream-pink of the light-struck areas, with the blues and reds (and some green) of the shadows, for both here and in the following picture, the harmonies of like colors has given way to the harmonies of contrasts more typical of Neo-Impressionism.

60

ROOFTOPS AND CITY STREET (LA RUE SAINT-VINCENT,
SOLEIL D'HIVER). 1889–1890.
Oil on canvas, 25 3/4 × 32″ (65.4 × 81.3 cm.).
Signed and dated l.r. "Lucien Pissarro 1890".

Early exhibition: Paris, Indépendants, 20 March – 27 April
1890, no. 621 ("La rue Saint-Vincent, soleil d'hiver").

Lent by Hirschl & Adler Galleries, Inc., New York.

In recent years the picture has borne the title of *Village Street,*
but one can see in the left background that the buildings
continue out of sight. It is probably *La Rue Saint-Vincent,
Winter Sun* exhibited in the spring of 1890, and this would
be logical for several reasons. The wan sun and grey sky
give a feeling of late November or early December; the Rue
Saint-Vincent is in just such surroundings on Montmartre
(then a little less congested than at present); Lucien was
close to Maximilien Luce who had his studio just one block
away, on the Rue Cortot. There is also some further evidence.
W. S. Meadmore, who had access to Lucien's papers [see
above, p. 50], paraphrases a letter he wrote to his future
wife in London: "He had been to Paris, had sent two of his
paintings of the Eragny countryside to the Exhibition of the

Indépendants, and had painted a picture from a window in
Monmartre [sic]; now he was invited to show at the Twenty
Group in Brussels." Although Meadmore seems to suggest
that the letter is of late 1890, it is of a year earlier, for Lucien
was invited in the autumn of 1889 to appear at Les XX in
February, 1890, and in the spring of 1890 he exhibited at
the Indépendants the three pictures referred to, "621. *La rue
Saint-Vincent, soleil d'hiver;* 266. *Prairies à Gisors, temps
gris;* 623. *Prairies à Thierceville, temps gris.*" The picture
done from a window in Montmartre is surely this one. The
light, although weak, is strong enough to color the walls
yellow, an effect the artist heightens by emphasizing the
complementary blue-lavender in the adjacent shaded areas.
Close examination reveals that almost every spectral color
appears in each area, but in proportions that permit a few
to dominate from a slight distance.

Jeanne Selmersheim-Desgrange
(1877–1958)

Jeanne Desgrange was born into a family in which the women had been artists and costume designers, the men architects and draftsmen. She began in the decorative arts herself then, after her marriage to Selmersheim was terminated (she retained the name), she met Paul Signac and became his second wife. Although she had had considerable training already, it was Signac who became her teacher, and her art is very close to his. She exhibited regularly at the Indépendants beginning in 1909. The rare references to her are found in the occasional exhibitions of Neo-Impressionism in which she appeared: Braun, in 1932; Beaux-Arts, in 1933–1934; J.-C. and J. Bellier, in 1961. In addition, she, Ginette Signac and their maternal forebears were given a joint exhibition at Saint-Jeoire-en-Faucigny early in 1967.

61
GARDEN AT "LA HUNE", SAINT-TROPEZ. 1909.

Oil on canvas, 25 × 31 7/8″ (63.5 × 81 cm.).
Signed and dated l.r. "J. Selmersheim-Desgrange 1909".

Collection Mr. and Mrs. W. J. Holliday, Indianapolis.

Georges Pierre Seurat
(1859–1891)

By the quality of his art and by being first to use divided
color laid down in small, regular brushstrokes, Seurat has
always been regarded as the chief Neo-Impressionist. The
son of a wealthy property owner, he was given a regular
allowance, and this spared him the cares of Luce, Hayet and
Lucien Pissarro, who had to patch together their lives with
a miscellany of jobs and part-time study. Seurat was already
a full-time art student by the age of fifteen, when he
enrolled in a municipal school near his home in Paris. At
eighteen he was taking classes at the Ecole des Beaux-Arts
with Henri Lehmann. His twentieth year was spent in
military service at Brest, and when he returned to Paris in
November, 1880, he had put all formal study behind him.
Drawings signed 1881 show him already to be an artist of
complete maturity, and his velvety conté crayon compositions,
following in the tradition of Rembrandt, Goya, Millet and
Daumier, rival these and other great masters. His early work
in oils (1881–1882) owed more to Corot, Millet, and the
Barbizon masters than to the Impressionists; in the same
years he saturated himself in the writings and paintings of
Delacroix, and treatises on composition and color theory by
Chevreul, Charles Blanc, and Ogden Rood, consciously
searching for a method of what he called "optical painting".
By 1883 the impact of the Impressionists, especially Monet,
Pissarro and Renoir, is visible in his paintings. He gradually
turned, too, from subjects of rural landscape and peasants
to suburban and city themes, and in 1884 at the first
Indépendants, showed his monumental *Bathing Place,
Asnières*. Together with Signac, Dubois-Pillet, Angrand and
Cross, he helped found and sustain the Indépendants, and
served on various committees until his death.

In the wake of his meeting with Signac, who acted as
intermediary with the older Impressionists and their art,
Seurat heightened his palette further and rapidly developed
the interwoven color-textures that crystallized Neo-
Impressionism. After the summer of 1885 at Grandcamp, on
the Channel coast, during which he began to use the finely
divided brushwork, he met Pissarro who became the first
convert. By the following spring, Signac and Pissarro's son
Lucien joined to form the nucleus of the group, and the four
exhibited side by side in the last Impressionist exhibition in
May. Seurat's *Grande Jatte* was the most controversial
painting in that exhibition, and it brought him instant
notoriety. He and his colleagues were adopted by Félix
Fénéon, Paul Adam, Gustave Kahn, and other Symbolist
writers, and Neo-Impressionism became the style of the
second half of the decade.

Seurat had the reputation of being withdrawn, but he

partook in the feverish activity in literary and artistic circles, and regularly attended the various soirées at the offices of the Symbolist reviews or in the homes of friends. He exhibited every year with the Indépendants, and with Les XX in Brussels, in 1887, 1889 and 1891. The power of his temperament and of his art were such that almost everyone who came into contact with him, worked for a time in his style, including Van Gogh and Emile Bernard. Except for 1887, when he spent part of the summer in military service, Seurat went to the Channel coast for the summer: to Honfleur in 1886, Port-en-Bessin in 1888, Le Crotoy in 1889, Gravelines in 1890. The greater part of the year was spent in Paris, where he refined his summer landscapes for exhibition, and worked on his succession of monumental canvases, *The Parade*, *The Models*, *Le Chahut*, *The Circus*. He also did a number of crayon drawings, which he regularly exhibited with his paintings.

Throughout these later years, he compounded his interest in color theory with a concern for the emotional associations of linear structure. Charles Blanc, whom he had read as a boy, had discussed such theories, and Seurat had found them elsewhere. It seems most likely that the rather exotic scientist Charles Henry, whom he met in the spring of 1886, renewed this long-standing interest. Color continued to be the chief public concern in Seurat's work, because of the conspicuous technique, but he himself turned increasingly to the associative theories. Their presence is felt in the linear structure and the subjects of his later paintings, which are marked by lively arabesques and the movement of urban entertainments, far from the monumentality of the *Grande Jatte*. At the time of his sudden death of acute diphtheria on March 29, 1891 (he was only thirty-one years and four months old), Seurat had made himself a major force in the evolution of modern art. His life's work was remarkably complete: over 240 oil paintings, several hundred drawings, of which about 250 rank with the greatest of any period, and a body of theory vested in his art and in his contact with others. Both the art and the theory have had a rich life in this century.

Exhibitions devoted to Seurat began with a little show at the *Revue Indépendante* early in 1888; he was given memorial exhibitions at Les XX in Brussels and the Indépendants in Paris in 1892, and apparently also at the *Revue Blanche* the same year; then, by Laffitte in 1895; *La Revue Blanche*, 1900; the Indépendants, 1905; Bernheim-Jeune in 1908 and 1920; Devambez, 1922; Brummer (New York), 1924; Lefèvre (London) and Bernheim-Jeune, both in 1926; Flechtheim (Berlin), 1928; Renaissance Society, University

of Chicago, 1935; Rosenberg, 1936; Buchholz (New York), 1947; Knoedler (New York), 1949; Galleria dell'Obelisco (Rome), 1950; Musée Jacquemart-André, 1957; Art Institute of Chicago and The Museum of Modern Art, New York, 1958. In addition, he has been in all group exhibitions of Neo-Impressionism, which sometimes have been little more than one-man exhibitions with a handful of pictures by his friends [see the general list of exhibitions].

Principal paintings in addition to those in the present exhibition include *Une Baignade, Asnières*, 1883–1884 (National Gallery, London); *Sunday Afternoon on the Island of the Grande Jatte*, 1884–1886 (Art Institute of Chicago); *The Models*, 1886–1888 (Barnes Foundation, Merion, Pennsylvania.); *Le Chahut*, 1888–1890 (Rijksmuseum Kröller-Müller, Otterlo); *La Poudreuse*, 1890 (Courtauld Collection, London); *The Circus*, 1890–1891 (Louvre).

Bibliography: See BIBLIOGRAPHY 1, 2, 3, 5, 6, 10, 11, 14, 18, 23, 26, 28, and C. M. de Hauke, *Seurat et son Oeuvre*, 2 vols., Paris, 1961 [catalogue raisonné of drawings and paintings]; Henri Dorra and John Rewald, *Seurat*, Paris, 1959 [catalogue raisonnée of paintings and the drawings related to them]; Robert L. Herbert, *Seurat's Drawings*, New York, 1962 [catalogues some drawings not in de Hauke]; John Rewald, *Seurat*, Paris, 1948, and *The History of Impressionism*, Museum of Modern Art, 1946 *et seq.*; Jean Sutter, "Georges Seurat" in BIBLIOGRAPHY 2.

99

"De Hauke catalogue" and "Dorra-Rewald catalogue" in the individual picture entries refer to those listed above.

62 (not illustrated)
STUDENT NOTEBOOK. 1877–1878.
Pencil, ink, charcoal and crayon, 3 3/8 × 5 7/8″ (8.5 × 15 cm.).

Formerly Edmond Aman-Jean.
Collection François Aman-Jean, Paris.

This notebook and the following one were identified by
Dr. Jean Sutter, who will assist in their first publication now
being prepared. The 40 pages in varied media have the style
of Seurat's work of 1877–1878.

63 (not illustrated)
TRAVEL NOTEBOOK. 1880.
Pencil, conté crayon and colored crayons, 4 1/4 × 7 1/2″
(11 × 19 cm.).

Formerly Edmond Aman-Jean.
Collection François Aman-Jean, Paris.

Seurat did military service at Brest, on the end of the Breton
peninsula, from November 1879 to November 1880. This
notebook is much like the "Brest notebook", long since
dismembered, but whose individual pages have been
catalogued. Two pages of this second sketchpad record the
itineraries of trips Seurat took in northern Brittany, and
51 are drawn on both sides in a great variety of subjects.

64

THE FOREST AT PONTAUBERT (SOUS-BOIS A
PONTAUBERT). 1881.
Oil on canvas, 30 1/2 × 24 1/2″ (77.5 × 62.2 cm.).
De Hauke catalogue 14 (dated c. 1882).
Dorra-Rewald catalogue 8 (dated "1880 ?").

Early exhibitions: Paris, La Revue Blanche, 19 March –
5 April 1900, hors catalogue; Paris, Bernheim-Jeune,
14 December 1908 – 9 January 1909, no. 6.

Formerly Emile Seurat; Alexandre Natanson; Otto van
Waetjen; Alfred Flechtheim; Julio Kocherthaler.
Collection Sir Kenneth Clark, London.

The most ambitious painting by Seurat before the *Baignade*
of 1883–1884, this picture has not been exhibited since 1909.
Pontaubert is in the valley of the Cousin river in central
France, a region much favored by Daubigny and Corot.
Together with his friend Aman-Jean, Seurat spent several
weeks there in late summer and early autumn, 1881. The
painting most resembles Corot, but the shimmering brushwork recalls also Théodore Rousseau and Diaz. Many
observers have felt that the only explanation for the dabbed
texture is a later reworking by the artist, but this does not
seem to be the case. Instead, it is a perfectly logical out-

growth of Seurat's immersion in Barbizon style. The pigments
are those he used in 1881–1882, and not the ones of 1883
and after. There are several earth tones, a russet color and
an olive green, and he has not yet begun to use the wine
reds, lavenders, pale blues and blue-greens he later favored.
Since a number of the dabs supposedly added later are of
the earth tones, one must assume that they were a part of
the picture from the beginning. Moreover, close examination
shows the following, integral method:

Taking the left foreground as an example, we find that there
was a brown undercoating which still shows through here
and there. Over this, Seurat softly stroked and dabbed some
green, in a very dilute mixture so that it acquired little physical
substance. On top of the first green, he then added several
greens, mixed in different proportions on the palette with
yellow and white. Next he introduced a few sparse dabs of
blue and pink, and a great deal of orange-tan and yellow-
tan. On the still thin surface, here and there he dragged a
brush heavily loaded with yellow-tan: the weave of the
canvas picked up tiny bits of the color, which might appear
as separate strokes, but are in reality parts of broad movements of the hand. They show, even in reproduction, in the
lower left corner, the left-central portion and the area to the
right of the central tree.

65

TWO WOMEN (DEUX FEMMES). c. 1882–1883.
Conté crayon, 11 3/4 × 9″ (29.7 × 22.9 cm.).
De Hauke catalogue 648 (dated c. 1885).

Formerly Emile Seurat; Camille Pissarro; Alphonse Bellier;
Ernest de Frenne; Mrs. C. J. Sullivan.
Collection Dr. and Mrs. John J. Mayers, Bronxville, New York.

The contrast between the thin, housewifely figure on the
left and the stout, plebeian laundress on the right is provided
by showing one in profile, the other from behind, and by
reversing the background so that the one is light on dark, the
other dark upon light.

66

THE DRAWBRIDGE (LE PONT-LEVIS). c. 1882–1883.
Conté crayon, 9 × 11 1/4″ (22.9 × 28.5 cm.).
De Hauke catalogue 608 (dated c. 1884).

Early exhibition: Paris, Bernheim-Jeune, 14 December 1908 –
9 January 1909, no. 113.

Formerly Mr. and Mrs. Samuel A. Lewisohn.
Collection Mrs. Joan Simon, New City, New York.

This is perhaps the finest of a number of drawings of
industrial and commercial sites that Seurat made. The
slashing forms have much of the passion that Franz Kline
invested in his large paintings a half-century later.

67

PLACE DE LA CONCORDE, WINTER. c. 1882–1883.
Conté crayon, 9 1/8 × 12 1/8″ (23.2 × 30.7 cm.).
De Hauke catalogue 564 (dated c. 1883).

Early exhibitions: Munich, Frankfort, Dresden, Karlsruhe,
Stuttgart, September 1906 – January 1907, "Französische
Künstler", no. 106; Paris, Bernheim-Jeune, 14 December
1908 – 9 January 1909, no. 115.

Formerly Félix Fénéon.
Collection The Solomon R. Guggenheim Museum, New York.

Seurat has chosen one of the rare snowfalls in Paris to
exploit his love of chiaroscuro. The snow is already soiled
by the tracks of carriages; it is early twilight, but the
streetlights are not yet lit, and their lamps are lost in the rich
grey of the air. The white is untouched paper; the tracks are
slashes of crayon; the lamps disappear on their stems because
Seurat drew the horizon arbitrarily down over them.

69
FARM LABORER WITH HOE (L'HOMME A LA HOUE).
c. 1882.
Oil on canvas, 18 1/8 × 22″ (46 × 55.8 cm.).
De Hauke catalogue 103 (dated c. 1884).
Dorra-Rewald catalogue 42 (dated c. 1882).

Early exhibitions: Paris, La Revue Blanche, 19 March –
5 April 1900, no. 8; Paris, Bernheim-Jeune, 14 December
1908 – 9 January 1909, no. 29.

Formerly Emilo Sourat; "Mme. J. D."; Mme. Camille Platteel;
Félix Fénéon.
Collection The Solomon R. Guggenheim Museum, New York.

Both Millet and Pissarro are brought to mind. The figure is
closer to Millet, but the overall effect is more like such a
picture as *Père Melon Sawing Wood* of 1879 [Pissarro-
Venturi 499]. Seurat discards the complexity of Pissarro's
surface movements, however, and by virtue of the oblique
angle of the sun, he lays out the prominent horizontal bars.
These serve two functions, one is to attach themselves to the
principal verticals and diagonals, the other is to subdivide
the surface into geometric zones. Both force the viewer's
attention on the laws of pictorial order as much as upon the
subject.

70

SEATED WOMAN (PAYSANNE ASSISE). c. 1883.
Oil on canvas, 15 × 18″ (38.1 × 45.7 cm.).
De Hauke catalogue 59 (dated c. 1883).
Dorra-Rewald catalogue 29 (dated 1882).

Early exhibition: Paris, Bernheim-Jeune, 14 December 1908 –
9 January 1909, no. 8.

Formerly Léo Gausson; Félix Fénéon.
Collection The Solomon R. Guggenheim Museum, New York.

Seurat's early training, which concentrated so much on the
human figure, begins to merge with his landscape study
until, in 1883–1884, he painted his first canvas of mural
scale, *Bathing Place, Asnières*. This small canvas has the
palette, the technique and the feeling of the large painting.
The woman has the simplified form of two artists Seurat
admired, Puvis de Chavannes and Millet. The brushstrokes
help construct the curving planes of her body, but the
meadow is painted with what Seurat called "broomswept"
strokes. They are closest, perhaps, to Camille Pissarro of the
same period, say the sky of his *Cours-La-Reine* of 1883
[no. 48], and Pissarro also painted in these years a number
of peasant women seated or standing in fields. The
distinctive note we attach to Seurat and to no other is the

direct placing of the enigmatic figure against the unified
background. How awkward it would be if the sky intruded
itself at the top.

68

HOUSE WITH THE RED ROOF (LA MAISON AU TOIT
ROUGE). c. 1882.
Oil on wood, 6 3/8 × 9 7/8" (16.2 × 25 cm.).
De Hauke catalogue 55 (dated c. 1883).
Dorra-Rewald catalogue 73 (dated c. 1883).

Formerly Zborowski; Percy Moore Turner; Lord Ivor Spencer
Churchill; Gaston Lévy; Victor Bossuat.
Private collection, France.

The horizontal bands of the previous drawing are transformed
here into zones of alternating light and dark, and the black
crayon into a rich variety of colored pigments. It was
probably painted in 1882, and represents a change from the
palette of the Pontaubert canvas [no. 64]. Earth colors are
gone, and if the pigments do not yet have the intensity of
1883, they are nonetheless placed in stronger oppositions.
In the winter of 1881–1882, Seurat had made excerpts from
Delacroix' writings, and color notes on some of his paintings,
stressing the use of opposed hues; in texts by Chevreul and
Rood he had found the same principles discussed at length.
If the shadow area of the foliage in the right foreground is
taken as an example, we can find the relationship to
Delacroix' practice and to theory, and we can explain why

red, seldom "seen" in green foliage, is so prominent:

A given color will surround itself with a halo of its own
color-opposite, Chevreul's law called "successive contrast",
hence red, blue and purple are in the tree's shaded portion
because they are the opposites of the green, orange and
yellow of the field (the orange and yellow there represent
reflected and partly-absorbed sunlight). As a result of
painting in this way, Chevreul's other famous law is invoked,
"simultaneous contrast", that is, the mutual exaltation of
opposites when placed side by side. The key to the picture's
harmony of opposites is found in the red roof that sparkles
against green foliage. Among many texts that Seurat copied
was the recipe for a "Simler-scope", a simple sandwich of
blue and yellow glass. By looking through it at foliage, blue,
yellow and green are eliminated, leaving only the reds. One
wonders if Seurat tried such devices.

71
HORSES IN THE WATER, STUDY FOR "UNE BAIGNADE,
ASNIERES" (CHEVAL BLANC ET CHEVAL NOIR DANS
L'EAU). 1883
Oil on wood, 6 × 9 1/2" (15.2 × 24.8 cm.).
De Hauke catalogue 86 (dated c. 1883).
Dorra-Rewald catalogue 88 (dated 1883–1884).

Early exhibition: Paris, La Revue Blanche, 19 March –
5 April 1900, no. 6.

Formerly Mme. Seurat mère; Percy Moore Turner; Samuel
Courtauld.
Collection The Dowager Lady Aberconway, London.

72
FINAL STUDY FOR "UNE BAIGNADE, ASNIERES". 1883.
Oil on wood, 6 1/4 × 9 3/4" (15.9 × 24.8 cm.).
Signed (?) l.r. "Seurat".
De Hauke catalogue 93 (dated c. 1883).
Dorra-Rewald catalogue 97 (dated 1883–1884).

Formerly Robert Caze; Gary; Sprenger; Dr. and Mrs.
David M. Levy.
Collection The Art Institute of Chicago.

Seurat's several studies for *Bathing Place, Asnières*
constitute a veritable apprenticeship to Impressionism. His
pictures of 1882 show already an awareness of the style
that was still controversial, but it was in 1883 that he began
to turn away from peasant and rural subjects to the closer
suburbs of Paris, adapting himself to the style as well as
to the subjects of Impressionism. Manet, Monet, and Renoir
are echoed in his little panels. *Horses in the Water* [no. 71]
is very close to Renoir's *Oarsmen at Chatou* of 1879
[National Gallery, Washington] with much the same palette
and the very same composition.

This panel is a composite of the separate sketches, and a
comparison with the previous one offers a ready lesson in
Seurat's manner of working. The varied brushwork of the
other, and its indefinite form, have been supplanted by
another kind of pictorial order. Already one feels, even in the
tiny panel, the grand scale of the human figure of the final
painting.

73

RIVER LANDSCAPE WITH TURRET (PAYSAGE A LA
TOURELLE). c. 1884.
Oil on wood, 6 1/8 × 9 3/4" (15.6 × 24.8 cm.).
De Hauke catalogue 96 (dated c. 1884).
Dorra-Rewald catalogue 106 (dated c. 1884).

Early exhibitions: Paris, Indépendants (Seurat retrospective),
19 March – 27 April 1892, no. 1113; Paris, La Revue
Blanche, 19 March – 5 April 1900, hors catalogue.

Formerly Emile Seurat; Alexandre Natanson; Gaston Lévy;
Victor Bossuat.
Private collection, France.

Until 1932, this was one side of a panel whose other side
was the *Rose Landscape* now in the Louvre; the two were
sawed apart that year and have had separate histories since.

The golden-brown panel color is used extensively as part of
the landscape mass, and it helps form the reflections in the
water, as well. This corresponds to the Barbizon practice of
working from dark towards light, and not the Impressionist
method of painting on a light ground.

74

WOMAN WITH MONKEY, STUDY FOR THE "GRANDE
JATTE" (LA FEMME AU SINGE). 1884.
Oil on wood, 9 3/4 × 6 1/4" (24.7 × 15.7 cm.).
De Hauke catalogue 137 (dated 1884–1885).
Dorra-Rewald catalogue 134 (dated 1884–1885).

Formerly Jean Ajalbert; Mrs. Cornelius J. Sullivan.
Collection Smith College Museum of Art, Northampton,
Massachusetts.

75

STUDY FOR THE "GRANDE JATTE" (PETITE ESQUISSE).
1884.
Oil on wood, 6 1/4 × 9 3/4" (15.9 × 24.8 cm.).
De Hauke catalogue 120 (dated 1884–1885).
Dorra-Rewald catalogue 128 (dated 1884–1885).

Formerly J. B. Stang.
Collection Mr. and Mrs. Howard J. Sachs, Stamford.

Some of the many panels for the famous painting now in
Chicago were done on the site, but others, like this one,
were painted in the studio and are composite studies. It is
one of the most complex of the small sketches, with a larger
number of figures than usual. One purpose of such a study
was to test the disposition of the figures; in the final painting,
the idea of the two seated groups in the foreground was
retained, but with considerable alteration.

The woman fishing, to the left, can remind us of the
relationship with Seurat's early drawings. Her sunlit side is
in a cream color, the adjacent water darkened to oppose it;
her shaded side is given an arbitrary golden yellow halo for
the same purpose, the whole constituting an alternation of
dark-light-dark-light that is the basis of so many of his

early crayon drawings. Furthermore, the solemn, erect figure
is that same human form which he had drawn as the very
basis of his study in the Ecole des Beaux-Arts, the classicizing
figure which he will insert into the park scene to produce his
monumental revision of Impressionism.

77

THE NURSE, STUDY FOR THE "GRANDE JATTE"
(LA NOUNOU). 1884–1885.
Conté crayon, 9 1/4 × 12 1/4" (23.5 × 31.2 cm.).
De Hauke catalogue 630 (dated 1884–1885).
Dorra-Rewald catalogue 138c (dated 1884–1885).

Early exhibitions: Paris, Indépendants (Seurat retrospective),
24 March – 30 April 1905, no. 8; Paris, Bernheim-Jeune,
14 December 1908 – 9 January 1909, no. 187.

Formerly Félix Fénéon; John Quinn; A. Conger Goodyear.
Collection Albright-Knox Art Gallery, Buffalo,
Gift of A. Conger Goodyear.

The beauty of such drawings resides in the distillation of
form, the elimination of the casual in favor of the iconic. The
nurse is seen rigidly from behind; her left contour and
vertical axis repeat the rhythm of the tree trunk; the obtuse
angle formed by the tree is all the more independent of
conventional associations because no foliage shows at the
top, and without knowing the final picture, one could not
tell that the black square from which it springs is a man's
tophat; Seurat has suppressed the second tree, part of which
once showed alongside this one in an early oil, but he has
retained its shadow. The severe forms thus established are

in the lineage of Piero della Francesca, Greek sculpture, and
Egyptian relief and wall painting. In the processional rhythms
of the completed painting, Seurat brought together this
age-old tradition with that of Impressionism, fusing drawing
with painting, black-and-white with color.

76

FINAL SKETCH FOR "SUNDAY AFTERNOON ON THE
ISLAND OF THE GRANDE JATTE" (ESQUISSE D'EN-
SEMBLE). 1884.
Oil on canvas, 27 3/4 × 40 5/8" (70.5 × 104.2 cm.).
Painted border by Seurat.
De Hauke catalogue 142 (dated 1884–1885).
Dorra-Rewald catalogue 138 (dated 1884–1885).

Early exhibitions: New York, Durand-Ruel, "Impressionists
of Paris", March 1886 – May 1886, hors catalogue; Paris,
Indépendants (Seurat retrospective), 19 March – 28 April
1892, no. 1088; Paris, La Revue Blanche, 19 March –
5 April 1900, no. 16; Paris, Indépendants (Seurat retrospective) 24 March – 30 April 1905, no. 5; Munich,
Frankfort, Dresden, Karlsruhe, Stuttgart, September 1906 –
January 1907, "Französische Künstler", no. 99; Paris,
Bernheim-Jeune, 14 December 1908 – 9 January 1909,
no. 45; Paris, Bernheim-Jeune, "La Faune", December 1910.

Formerly Léon Appert; Félix Fénéon; Adolphe Lewisohn;
Samuel A. Lewisohn.
Collection The Metropolitan Museum of Art, New York
Bequest of Samuel A. Lewisohn, 1951.

The final composition in Chicago was repainted in the winter
and spring of 1885–1886 in unstable pigments which
Camille Pissarro had advised Seurat to use. These changed
so badly that several critics noted by 1892 the number of
alterations that had already taken place, for example, bright
oranges had turned to olive-browns. The large sketch has
colors which are, therefore, closer to Seurat's original
intention than the Chicago painting in its present condition.

In a letter of 1890 to Fénéon [in several manuscript versions,
collections John Rewald and the estate of C. M. de Hauke],
Seurat gave the sequence of events involving the picture:
On Ascension Day, August 15, 1884, he was already at
work on the big oil; in December he exhibited the unpeopled
landscape of the site [Mr. and Mrs. John Hay Whitney];
in March the final canvas was ready for exhibition, but the
Indépendants' show did not take place after all that spring
and so the picture was not seen then; in October, 1885, he
met Pissarro and began to repaint the picture using the
unstable pigments of a certain "Maître Edouard"; it was
finally shown in May, 1886. From this we can deduce the
following: The early panels were done in the spring and
summer of 1884, probably including the Sachs picture

[no. 75]. The composition was far enough advanced in August to begin work on the big picture, but this must have consisted of blocking in the principal elements in schematic form. Next he must have turned to the present picture, in order to test certain colors and patterns in a handier size, and he also must have returned to the site, at least into early autumn, to make further studies from nature. As the forms of the large canvas began to be refined, he then did most of the crayon drawings [no. 77], in order to provide the exact shapes that he would use.

The colors and the simplified forms of the large sketch lie underneath the finished picture, and it is fascinating to see how Seurat worked. He used a brownish undercoating common to mid-century painting, rather than the white favored by the Impressionists. This left him on familiar ground, because he normally worked on the varnish-brown surface of his wood panels, and here as well as there, he let the brown form part of the darker tones and of the faces of most of the figures. In the sun-struck area of the grass, for example, the brown acts as a stable substructure. Over this he first put several medium and light greens, then more of the same, plus yellow-green, yellow, pale orange-tan, orange

and light blue. The blue is the only contrasting tone used, because (to speak of theory) as the opposite of sunlight's orange-yellow, it is the one color reaction not obliterated by full sun. In shade, on the other hand, weak sunlight permits a greater variety of reactions. For the dog in the foreground, Seurat first brushed in an orange-red over the undercoating. This shows through between the surface strokes of wine reds, blues, purple, green and orange-red, but confers only a unity of area, not of hue; no one color results from these juxtapositions.

The visual excitement generated by the colors in this chopped-straw technique tends to disguise the remarkable monumentality of the composition, which the tiny strokes of the finished picture helped bring out.

78
LIGHTHOUSE AT HONFLEUR (LE PHARE DE HONFLEUR).
1886.
Conté crayon, 9 1/4 × 11 3/4″ (23.5 × 29.8 cm.).
De Hauke catalogue 656.
Dorra-Rewald catalogue 163a.

Formerly Emile Seurat; Félix Fénéon; Mr. and Mrs. John
Rewald
The Lehman Collection, New York.

79
EVENING, HONFLEUR (HONFLEUR, UN SOIR,
EMBOUCHURE DE LA SEINE). 1886.
Oil on canvas, 25 1/4 × 31 1/2″ (64 × 80 cm.).
Signed l.r. "Seurat".
Wooden frame painted by Seurat.
De Hauke catalogue 167.
Dorra-Rewald catalogue 171.

Early exhibitions: Brussels, Les XX, February 1887, no. 7;
Paris, Indépendants, 26 March – 3 May 1887, no. 441;
Brussels, Les XX, February 1892, no. 8; Antwerp, L'Associa-
tion pour l'Art, November 1892, no. 3.

Formerly Madeleine Knoblock; Gustave Kahn; Victor
Claessens; Armand Claessens; Dr. and Mrs. David M. Levy.
Collection Museum of Modern Art, New York,
Gift of Mrs. David M. Levy.

Honfleur had been much favored by Courbet, Jongkind and
Monet, and Seurat was following in their wake in his
successive painting campaigns along the Channel coast. This
picture is closest to Monet, whose *Falaises des Petites Dalles*
of 1880 [Museum of Fine Arts, Boston] is the prototype. The

younger man's vision is found in the melancholy stillness of the scene, an effect enhanced by eliminating Monet's prominent cliff in the background, permitting the sky to stretch itself over much more of the surface. A number of the Symbolists were particularly fond of Seurat's seascapes. Joris-Karl Huysmans wrote [in *La Revue Indépendante*, April 1887] that his Honfleur paintings rested

■ on this particular feeling that he expresses of a nature more lulling than melancholy, a nature which reposes indifferently under skies without passion, sheltered from the winds. Those who wish are free to prefer less cold and more vivid impressions, or to love beaches more bustling and noisy; for me these works have a particular charm which I cannot at all deny. I find in them a fullness of expansive air, a siesta of a quiet soul, a distinction of wan indolence, a caressing lullaby of the sea which soothes and dissipates my weary cares.

Begun at Honfleur in the summer, this painting was finished over the autumn and winter. The myth that later sprang up, according to which Seurat used only the primary colors, can

be easily destroyed by examining the painting. About 25 different tones, mixed on the palette, can be found. In the lower left foreground, many dark dots of pigment are placed in the center of larger discs, precisely as in Lucien Pissarro's landscape of the same year [no. 55], and in his own studies [Louvre] for *The Models*. However, far from being composed uniformly of dots, the surface is built up of larger strokes over a tan-brown undercoating. In the sky, one easily sees large and freely-brushed strokes with only the darker elements rendered in actual dots.

The painted frame was added by Seurat, perhaps in the early summer of 1887 when Lucien Pissarro wrote his father and Signac about Seurat's new experiments. Seurat himself had written Signac the previous summer about the borders he was painting directly on the canvas, and this was the next step. Pissarro and Whistler had painted their frames earlier, both in contrasting and in harmonizing tones, but with none of the complexity of Seurat's.

80
STUDY FOR "LES POSEUSES". 1886–1887.
Oil on wood, 6 3/8 × 8 3/4" (16.2 × 22.2 cm.).
Painted borders by Seurat.
De Hauke catalogue 180 (dated 1887).
Dorra-Rewald catalogue 177 (dated 1886–1887).

Early exhibitions: Paris, Indépendants (Seurat retrospective),
24 March – 30 April 1905, no. 22; Paris, Bernheim-Jeune,
14 December 1908 – 9 January 1909, no. 65.

Formerly Paul Signac.
Private collection, Paris.

The intellectualization that Seurat's art calls for is lost when
actually looking at this tiny panel. It is in the lineage of
Fouquet and the great illuminators of the French tradition.
The intensity of beauty it generates is a compound of its
simple but elegant composition and the rich colors that
compose fleetingly in our eye, then fade, only to return in
altered tones.

After he had painted the three nudes separately [no. 81 and
two others in the Louvre], Seurat tried out the whole
composition on this panel. Then he made a series of drawings
to define the forms precisely, adding several still-life

elements to the foreground before he carried the large
canvas [Barnes Foundation, Merion, Pennsylvania] very far.
The painted borders on the sides of the composition here are
wine-red, on the left, against the greens of the *Grande Jatte*
(which serves as a background for the models), and green, on
the right, against the violets of the wall. They are a preliminary
statement of the painted frame, subsequently lost, for the big
picture, but which was commented upon by the Pissarros,
Signac and many contemporary critics. Within the composition, the brown of the panel is used as an element of the
color, but the final picture was painted on white gesso.

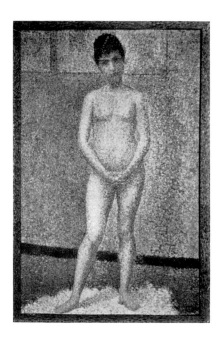

81

THE MODEL (POSEUSE DE FACE). 1886–1887; 1890.
Oil on wood, 10 1/4 × 6 3/4" (26 × 17.2 cm.).
Signed l.r. "Seurat".
Inner frame painted by Seurat in 1890.
De Hauke catalogue 183 (dated 1887).
Dorra-Rewald catalogue 174 (dated 1886–1887; 1890).

Early exhibitions: Paris, Indépendants, 26 March – 3 May
1887, no. 446; Paris, Indépendants (Seurat retrospective),
19 March – 27 April 1892, no. 1116; Paris, La Revue
Blanche, 19 March – 5 April 1900, no. 29; Paris, Indépendants (Seurat retrospective), 24 March – 30 April 1905,
no. 11; Paris, Bernheim-Jeune, 14 December 1908 –
9 January 1909, no. 68; Paris, Bernheim-Jeune, "Nus",
17–28 May 1910, no. 108; Berlin, Secession, 1913, no. 227.

Formerly Félix Fénéon.
Collection Musée du Louvre, Galeries du Jeu de Paume, Paris.

One of the principal reasons for Seurat's tiny brushstroke
was his wish for infinite nuance in his colors. The wall, "in
reality" one color, has several transformations of hue as,
chameleon-like, it reacts to the painted frame and to the two
sides of the nude. There were other reasons also, besides the
somewhat misunderstood "optical mixture", which is really
the *failure* to mix completely that resulted in the vibration of
color the artist sought. They include the even drying that is
a benefit of using small particles of pigment rather than thick
strokes, and the wilful, reasoned neutrality of the texture, as
distinct from the "romantic" brushwork of the Impressionists.

This figure is nearly identical in pose and outline to drawings
of the live model which Seurat had made a decade earlier,
and others after classical statues. The matter-of-fact posing
of three studio models in the final painting is a result of
thinking first of the isolated human body, the very basis of
the humanistic tradition in which he had been schooled, and
then of the juxtaposition of three of them in one composition
(here, the towel on the floor recalls the round pedestal the
Ecole models stood on). Contemporaries saw the relationship
with Ingres and the classical tradition, but they did not see
the parallel with Renoir, who in these very same years had
turned to Ingres and classical art in reaction against the
Impressionists' devotion to the present moment.

82

LA PARADE (UNE PARADE DE CIRQUE). 1886–1888.
Oil on canvas, 39 1/4 × 59 1/4" (99.7 × 150 cm.).
De Hauke catalogue 187 (dated 1888).
Dorra-Rewald catalogue 181 (dated 1887–1888).

Early exhibitions: Paris, Indépendants, 22 March – 3 May
1888, no. 614; Brussels, Les XX (Seurat retrospective),
February 1892, no. 10; Paris, Indépendants (Seurat
retrospective), 19 March – 27 April 1892, no. 1084; Paris,
La Revue Blanche, 19 March – 5 April 1900, no. 69; Paris
Bernheim-Jeune, 14 December 1908 – 9 January 1909,
no. 69.

Formerly Mme. Seurat mère; J. and G. Bernheim-Jeune;
Stephen C. Clark.
Collection The Metropolitan Museum of Art, New York.
Bequest of Stephen C. Clark, 1960.

One of Seurat's six largest canvases, *La Parade* is his most
enigmatic, and it is worth the effort to identify as many
elements as possible, not with the hope of reducing the
enigma, but in order to make it all the more mysterious. The
site is the Cirque Corvi, a fact known from contemporaries
and from illustrations by Jules Garnier, which show even the

tree with the very same branches. We are looking at the
wooden and canvas structure that projects in front of the
permanent building. On the left, the musicians play behind a
railing whose balusters towards the bottom are easily
confused with their legs. Behind the one to the right are two
large ovals, painted canvas backdrops usually picturing major
attractions of the circus. To the right of the trombonist the
repeated "O" is part of the figure 30 or 40, the price of
admission stencilled on paper or cardboard and tacked to a
vertical post or to the wall. This is behind the green plane to
the right, and the musicians would be able to turn to our
right and walk directly into the interior. Behind the
trombonist, there is a diagonal handrail along the steps that
give access to the platform. On the extreme right, a woman
is purchasing a ticket from the vendor whose face shows
behind the window; the woman's daughter is peering
through the booking wicket. Apparently the green rectangle
to the left of this same plane is a door folded back, but
above it, the darker tone seems to be the same as that of the
windows, and yet has no frame or edge. At the top, the gas
springs from a thin metal tube of about one-half inch
section which was clamped to wooden uprights in front of

the platform. Seurat has suppressed the uprights, apparently, for no views of the Corvi show an expanse like this with fewer than two.

As for the story being told, it is the preliminary show designed to attract customers. To the right of the trombonist are a clown, and the ringmaster (in an early drawing, there was a pony between them), standing on a platform that runs behind the central figure. The spectators are a cross-section of society. From left to right, with the aid of costume and Seurat's genius with silhouettes, we find a worker and his wife; two young women talking; a solitary figure common in Seurat's paintings (a kind of alter ego); a more elegant couple; a provincial in bowler hat, with his child; another middle-class couple; a pair of young lovers in the corner and, above them, the mother and daughter.

How much more the wonder, then, that from all this bustle and life, Seurat has composed a picture that has the stillness of a strange rite. He superimposed over actuality a passionate yearning for permanence, for that which endures, for contact with the past. The composition is based upon the Golden Section, the proportional ratio known to the Greeks and long favored in the classical tradition in French art. One feels that the arbitrariness of the horizontals and verticals are a mental structure more real to Seurat than the site. Egypt is recalled by the processional isolation of the figures, the combination of profile and frontal views in the trombonist and short clown, and their poses. Charles Blanc's *Grammar of the Arts of Design*, which Seurat read and annotated, has illustrations of Egyptian reliefs which may have formed an unconscious inspiration for *La Parade*, especially since they accompany a section in which Blanc discusses the relationship between architecture and feeling, and why "monumental architecture in flat sections expresses ideas of calm, fatality and duration", particularly when the horizontal elements are emphasized. These familiar ideas must have returned to Seurat's attention, because he was preoccupied with the related theories of Charles Henry, a scientist and esthetician whom he had met in 1886. Henry elaborated the earlier theories of emotional associations with certain linear movements: calm for horizontal, sad for downward, gay for upward. Seurat cited key phrases from his *Une Esthétique Scientifique* (1885) on a preliminary drawing for *La Parade*, among them, "abstraction—lines—direction".

83 (not illustrated)
SEURAT'S AUNT ANAIS HAUMONTE ON HER DEATHBED
(ANAIS HAUMONTE [1831–1887] SUR SON LIT DE
MORT). 1887.
Conté crayon, 9 7/8 × 12 5/8″ (25 × 32 cm.).
Signed l.r. "G.S.".

Previously uncatalogued and unpublished.
Private collection, France.

This drawing is one that moves us deeply, even from a
distance, before we can make out its subject. Then, when we
learn that it is a deathbed, and further, that it represents the
artist's aunt, we wonder what sort of man this was, who
could render the funeral room so detachedly? The answer is
in our first instinct: to find the composition moving as a
great work of art. Seurat ennobled the people he loved by
creating memorable images of them. As an artist, the act of
making a drawing was the natural way for him to record his
feelings, because art and life were so intertwined that they
were inseparable. Unlike the *Place de la Concorde* [no. 67],
whose scrawled horizontals and spiky verticals embody
movement and life within its melancholy quiet, the deathbed
has softer and more tender greys and blacks. The only
verticals are signs of afterlife—the cross and candles in the
background—and the only diagonal is formed by the unseen
face of the moribund, a luminous glow of white which
echoes the light of the candles, and which speaks for the
human intelligence that was there, unwilling to sink to the
final horizontal of the body.

Anaïs Haumonté, née Faivre, was the sister of Seurat's
mother, and intimately associated with his life. The two
sisters were constantly together and their families shared
vacations, so that the young Georges came to know her
as well as his parents. She died in November 1887, and
will be remembered because her nephew was an artist.

84
AU CONCERT EUROPEEN. 1887–1888.
Conté crayon with touches of gouache, 12 1/4 × 9 3/8″
(31 × 24 cm.).
Signed u.l. "Seurat".
De Hauke catalogue 689 (dated 1887–1888).

Early exhibitions: Paris, Indépendants, 22 March – 3 April
1888, no. 615; Brussels, Les XX, February 1889, no. 11;
Paris, Bernheim-Jeune, 14 December 1908 – 9 January 1909,
no. 177.

Formerly Charles Vignier, Théo Van Rysselberghe; Madeleine
Octave Maus; Gustave Gevaert; Edouard von der Heydt;
A. Flechtheim; Lillie P. Bliss.
Collection The Museum of Modern Art, New York,
Lillie P. Bliss Collection.

It was Daumier who established the type of composition in
which the observer is placed among the audience, looking
at the stage, and it was Degas who gave to it the richness
of his inventive mind. Degas was especially fond of the
café-concert, and would draw the observer into a varied
counterpoint of movements among the audience, with their
glances this way and that. Seurat revised Degas, just as in
his *Grande Jatte* he had revised Monet and Renoir. The four

figures seated in his café-concert have the solemnity of
worshippers at a religious service; instead of the sparkle of
varied movement, his composition is dominated by one
rhythm which runs from the wavy undulation of the chair
backs at the bottom, to the similar line of the shoulders
above, through the more agitated crests of the heads, and
finally is released by the bird-like rising and falling of the
singer's arms.

The café-concert was begun in Paris in the 1840s, but really
developed rapidly after 1867, when guild laws which had
limited the type of entertainment were finally removed. At
first the waiters circulated among ordinary tables and chairs
to serve drinks while the clients watched the small stage. At
the time of Seurat's drawing, the café-concert had become
so popular that it was equally common to have fixed seats
and large stages as in theaters, with the bar to the side.
(This form turned into the music hall in the 1890s, to suit the
ever larger urban population.)

85

PORT-EN-BESSIN, LES GRUES ET LA PERCEE. 1888.
Oil on canvas, 25 1/2 × 31 7/8" (65 × 81 cm.).
Signed l.r. "Seurat".
Border painted by Seurat.
De Hauke catalogue 190.
Dorra-Rewald catalogue 185.

Early exhibitions: Brussels, Les XX, February 1889, no. 9;
Paris, Indépendants, 20 March – 17 April 1890, no. 732;
Paris, Indépendants (Seurat retrospective), 19 March –
27 April 1892, no. 1102; Paris, La Revue Blanche, 1892;
Paris, Bernheim-Jeune, 14 December 1908 – 9 January 1909,
no. 72bis.

Formerly Mme. Seurat mère; Appert family; Félix Fénéon.
Collection The Honorable and Mrs. W. Averell Harriman,
New York.

Like *La Parade*, this landscape welds together present
observation, past part, and a will towards abstraction. The
compositions of Courbet and Monet are invoked, and the
established tradition of plein-air painting along the English
Channel. The fact that this is natural light, unlike the
artificial light which so interested Seurat in the *Parade*,
should not obscure the degree to which the work is an
artificial construction. At the base of the canvas and in the
sky are rhythmic undulations which make us think of similar
rhythms in Van Gogh's work, and of incipient Art Nouveau
in which Seurat shares. Many distinct shapes come forth
from the sky, and as it meets the hill on the left, it develops
a cream-colored halo. The strokes on the rolling land at that
point follow the direction of the halo, setting up a dialogue
of color and texture that speaks more of art than of nature.

No color theory can explain the painted border, which
sometimes contrasts with the contiguous area of the painting,
but at other times harmonizes with it. Seurat told his friends
that in such borders and frames he was trying to establish
an area of transition between the picture itself and its
environment.

86

THE EIFFEL TOWER. 1889.
Oil on wood, 9 1/2 × 6" (24 × 15 cm.).
Border painted by Seurat.
De Hauke catalogue 196 (dated 1889).
Dorra-Rewald catalogue 191 (dated 1889).

Early exhibition: Paris, Léonce Moline, "Exposition de
quelques Peintures . . . . de Ch. Agard, Eug. Delâtre,
J. H. Lebasque, feu Georges Seurat", 22 February — 14 March
1895.

Formerly Roger Marx; Marguerite Caetani.
Collection Mr. and Mrs. Germain Seligman, New York.

The sense of the *modern* which Seurat and the Neo-
Impressionists had (Hayet both drew and painted the tower)
was quite consistent. Seurat had admired Zola and Huysmans
in the early 1880s, when they called attention to the power
of modern industrial architecture, and he made drawings of
the industrial environment from about 1882 on [no. 66]. His
landscapes, even of the Channel ports, often contain elements
of homely contemporaneity rather than the historic buildings
and sites the tourists preferred. By and large the Eiffel tower
was condemned by conservatives and defended by the

young Symbolists whom Seurat counted as his friends. (In
La Revue Indépendante in 1887, Jules Laforgue had
championed the tower against a public protest signed by
Meissonier, Dumas, Lecomte de Lisle, Garnier, Gounod and
others.)

It was Meyer Schapiro who first spoke of the parallels
between Seurat's technique and the very concept of his art,
on the one hand, and the techniques and rationale of modern
engineering, on the other. Eiffel invented a special weather-
proof encaustic for his tower, in five shades from copper red
at the base to bright yellow at the top, and these account
for some of the variation in Seurat's panel (although the
tower had not yet reached its full height when he painted it).

87

LE CROTOY, AVAL. 1889.
Oil on canvas, 27 3/8 × 34" (70.5 × 86.4 cm.).
Signed l.r. "Seurat".
Border painted by Seurat.
De Hauke catalogue 195.
Dorra-Rewald catalogue 192.

Early exhibitions: Paris, Indépendants, 3 September –
3 October 1889, no. 241; Brussels, Les XX, February 1891,
no. 3; Brussels, Les XX (Seurat retrospective), February 1892,
no. 16; Paris, Indépendants (Seurat retrospective), 19 March –
27 April 1892, no. 1103; The Hague, Kunstkring, "Tentoonstilling van Schilderijen en Teekeningin van eenigen uit
de 'XX' en uit de 'Association pour l'Art'", July 1892, no. 34;
Antwerp, L'Association pour l'Art, November 1892, no. 5;
Paris, Bernheim-Jeune, 14 December 1908 – 9 January 1909,
no. 74; London, Grafton Galleries, "Manet and the Post-
Impressionists", 8 November 1910 – 15 January 1911,
no. 54; Paris, Bernheim-Jeune, "L'Eau", 26 June – 13 July
1911, no. 48.

Formerly Edmond Picard; Richard Goetz; M. Lowenstein;
Edward G. Robinson.
Niarchos collection, Athens.

The Hague exhibition of 1892 listed above, organized by
Jan Toorop and Henri Van de Velde, has not previously been
identified with Seurat. He showed also *The Lighthouse at
Honfleur* [Paul Mellon, Washington, D. C.], *A Corner of the
Harbor of Honfleur* [Rijksmuseum Kröller-Müller, Otterlo], and
Gravelines, Evening [no. 89].

88
PORTRAIT OF PAUL SIGNAC. 1889–1890.
Conté crayon, 13 1/2 × 11″ (34.5 × 28 cm.).
Originally signed l.l. "Seurat" on the glass frame.
De Hauke catalogue 694 (dated 1889–1890).

Early exhibitions: Paris, Indépendants, 20 March – 17 April 1890, no. 735B; Paris, Indépendants (Seurat retrospective), 19 March – 27 April 1892, no. 1124; Brussels, Les XX (Seurat retrospective), February 1892, no. 22; Paris, La Revue Blanche, 19 March – 5 April 1900, no. 52; Paris. Bernheim-Jeune, "Portraits d'hommes". 16 December 1907 – 4 January 1908, no. 122; Paris, Bernheim-Jeune, 14 December 1908 – 9 January 1909, no. 204.

Formerly Paul Signac.
Collection Mme. Ginette Signac, Paris.

Seurat's portraits are exclusively of his closest friends, Aman-Jean [Metropolitan Museum], Paul Alexis [Collection unknown], and Signac, and many of his drawings of the human figure were done after members of his family. His love for them is not shown in tender insights into character, nor expressions of feeling. Instead, he honors them by the dignity he creates for their images. Signac's portrait has the quality of Holbein. The curtain in the background reminds us of Holbein's *Sir Thomas More* [Frick Collection], and the cane, of the staffs held by many of More's contemporaries in the German master's portraits. Although Seurat had copied Holbein in his youth, and his *Aman-Jean* echoes the Louvre's *Erasmus of Rotterdam*, the relationship is a latent and unconscious one. Part of the portrait's feeling of ageless monumentality results from the absence of the usual attributes of an artist (palette, easel or bohemian costume), and the absence also of any hint of Signac's natural ebullience.

The portrait was reproduced on the cover of an issue of *Les Hommes d'Aujourd'hui* in 1890, devoted to Signac. Subsequent reproductions often show a double signature in the lower left corner, which is due to the fact that Seurat signed his name on the surface of the protective glass: photographs often captured both the signature and its shadow on the paper underneath. The irregular scratchy marks to the left appear on a number of Seurat's drawings, and appear to be the result of rubbing the crayon in order to remove a particle of foreign matter, or simply to sharpen it.

89

GRAVELINES, EVENING (LE CHENAL DE GRAVELINES,
UN SOIR). 1890.
Oil on canvas, 25 3/4 × 32 1/4″ (65.3 × 82 cm.).
Signed l.r. "Seurat".
Border painted by Seurat.
De Hauke catalogue 210.
Dorra-Rewald catalogue 203.

Early exhibitions: Brussels, Les XX, February 1891, no. 7;
Paris, Indépendants, 20 March – 27 April 1891, no. 1106;
Brussels, Les XX (Seurat retrospective), February 1892,
no. 17; Paris, Indépendants (Seurat retrospective), 19 March –
27 April 1892, no. 1107; The Hague, Kunstkring, "Tentoonstilling van Schilderijen en Teekeningen van eenigen uit
de 'XX' en uit de 'Association pour l'Art'", July 1892,
no. 35; Paris, Hôtel Brébant, "Les Néo-Impressionnistes",
2 December 1892 – 8 January 1893, no. 51; Vienna,
Sécession, January – February 1903, no. 117; Brussels,
Libre Esthétique (Seurat retrospective), February – March
1904, no. 117; Paris, Indépendants (Seurat retrospective),
24 March – 30 April 1905, no. 39; Paris, Bernheim-Jeune,
14 December 1908 – 9 January 1909, no. 81; Düsseldorf,
Galerie A. Flechtheim, 1913.

Formerly Madeleine Knoblock; Mme. Veuve Monnom;
Théo Van Rysselberghe; Rolf de Maré.
Collection Mr. and Mrs. William A. M. Burden, New York.

This is a "composed landscape" in the grand French
tradition. Its four surviving drawings and one oil study show
that the final composition is based upon several views in
which the principal elements of landscape remain constant,
but the boats and anchors are in various shapes and
positions. Shifting the man-made units about is parallel to
the pictorial game of chess Seurat had played with the
personages of the *Grande Jatte* six years before, but the
scarcity of drawings for earlier landscapes and their proximity
to photographs of the sites suggest that only in this summer
of 1890 was he beginning to take such liberties with
unpeopled landscapes. From the vantage point of the
Barbizon and Impressionist artists, the composed landscape
was anathema, and hence Pissarro said "Seurat is of the
Ecole des Beaux-Arts, he is steeped in it". Viewed from the
twentieth century, however, the same qualities in Seurat are
the source of our admiration.

Japonisme was among the several stylistic impulses Seurat
absorbed and then transformed for later artists. His evening

landscape and, even more, its oil study and other panels of
the same summer, are very close to the series of landscapes
from an album of Hiroshige's published the previous year
in Bing's *Le Japon Artistique* (vol. 24, 1889, pl. BFF). Color,
on the other hand, has nothing of the flat tones of Japanese
prints. Every spectral hue is present, with the infinite nuance
that was made possible by the fine brushwork. In contrast,
Gauguin and the Nabis, much taken with Japanese art, gave
relatively uniform colors to the flat zones of their paintings,
a logical relationship. And Cézanne, whose diagonal brushwork is as arbitrary as Seurat's, created architectonic surfaces
that suit the complexity of his shapes and spaces. Only
Seurat brought together so movingly a love of atmospheric
color with shapes that could be cut with tin snips.

Paul Signac
(1863–1935)

The opposite of Seurat in training and temperament, Signac
was almost entirely self-taught. Outgoing, even ebullient,
where Seurat was taciturn, Signac was the chief publicist
and public leader of Neo-Impressionism. He was born in
1863 of well-to-do shopkeepers in Paris, and was financially
independent all his life. In 1882 he turned to painting full
time but, except for a short period the following year in an
"atelier libre", he had no formal training. Instead he sought
out Impressionist paintings as guideposts, particularly
Monet's and Guillaumin's (traces of Pissarro and Jongkind
are also evident in his earliest landscapes). He met Seurat
in 1884, at the founding of the Société des Artistes
Indépendants. In the exchange that followed, Seurat offered
the reasoned certainty of his method and his theories, and
Signac introduced Seurat to the world of the Impressionists
and the young Symbolist writers. By the winter of 1885–1886,
both painters had met Camille Pissarro and his son Lucien,
with whom Signac's anarchist sympathies struck an
immediate chord. It was apparently Signac who introduced
Seurat and the Pissarros to Félix Fénéon, Gustave Kahn, Paul
Adam and other writers, and also to the older Paul Alexis,
friend of Zola and Cézanne, who was to become one of the
champions of Neo-Impressionism. In addition to the café
meetings of writers and painters, the soirées at Signac's
studio in Montmartre and occasional dinners at his home in
Asnières helped form close friendships in the years
1886–1888 between the two newest art groups, the Neo-
Impressionists and the Symbolists.

Signac, whose first pictures in small divided strokes were
done in the spring of 1886, joined Seurat and the two
Pissarros in the last Impressionist exhibition in May.
Relationships with Dubois-Pillet, Luce and Angrand were
strengthened, and Neo-Impressionism was well established
by the spring of 1887. Signac already had the role of
publicist, which fell to his lot as a natural result of his
extroverted personality. It was he who was chiefly responsible
for initiating Van Gogh into the mysteries of the new color,
and again he who established close communication with
Van Rysselberghe, Van de Velde and the Belgians who were
forming a second group of Neo-Impressionists. Signac
exhibited with Les XX in 1888 and 1890, and the following
year was made a foreign member of the Brussels exhibition
society.

In 1892, the year after Seurat's death, Signac began to go
regularly to Saint-Tropez on the Mediterranean. A born
sailor, he always kept one or more boats, and since his trip
to Port-en-Bessin in 1882, he had gone to the shore or
sometimes along the Seine, for summer campaigns of

painting. Until 1911, he used his villa at Saint-Tropez as a base for his warm-weather travels, which took him to Marseilles, Antibes, to Venice in 1904, and Constantinople in 1907. (He also made a trip to London in 1898, in the midst of a great enthusiasm for Turner and Ruskin.) At Saint-Clair, not far from Saint-Tropez, Henri-Edmond Cross had installed himself in the early 1890s. Signac had known him for years, but only after Seurat's death did they become intimate friends. Until Cross's death in 1910, they shared the duties of hosts to their many friends from Paris. This was particularly important in the years 1902–1906, when Valtat, Puy, Manguin, Marquet and others who formed the Fauve group visited them regularly. The most famous instance is Matisse's summer of 1904 with Signac, and the free adaptation of Neo-Impressionism that he formulated. Signac maintained a more public role, as well. Long Vice-President of the Indépendants, he was President from 1908 until a year before his death in 1935, and he helped insure the vitality of the exhibition society which welcomed the Fauves and later, the Cubists.

Signac was also an intermediary between the Neo-Impressionists and the public in his writings. He was close to the society of avant-garde writers and musicians of his day, a friend of Romain Rolland, Ernest Chausson, and Vincent d'Indy. He was a Beyliste, a member of the Stendhal society, and long worked on a book on the writer. He contributed prefaces to exhibitions, several of them quite important, and in 1927 wrote a book on Jongkind's watercolors. For the history of Neo-Impressionism, there are two brief periods that stand out. From 1888 to 1890 he collaborated with the esthetician Charles Henry, the very influential friend of Fénéon, Kahn and Seurat, and provided diagrams and illustrations for two of Henry's books published in 1890. Then, in 1895, he started to prepare his D'Eugène Delacroix au Néo-Impressionnisme which was published in La Revue Blanche in 1898, and in book form in 1899. In many ways a personal essay, it drew together much of nineteenth-century color theory and has rightly been considered the fundamental document of Neo-Impressionism. His art proper was at its very best in his marine paintings of the late 1880s and early 1890s, his large seaports of the Fauve period, and his late watercolors.

Besides appearing in all exhibitions of Neo-Impressionism, Signac has been given a great many one-man shows, by Bing in 1902; Cassirer (Berlin) in 1903; Druet in 1904; Bernheim-Jeune in 1907, 1911 [with Maillol], 1913, 1920, 1923, 1924–1925 [with Cross and Matisse], 1927, and 1930; Giroux (Brussels, with L. Cousturier), 1923; Marcel Bernheim [with Picart Le Doux], 1925; Wildenstein (London), 1934; Huinck en Scherjon (Amsterdam), 1935; Musée des Beaux-Arts, Mulhouse, 1950; Petit Palais [with Redon and Chaplet], 1950; Musée National d'Art Moderne, 1951; Fine Arts Associates (New York), 1951; Neuchâtel, 1952; Düsseldorf, 1953; Los Angeles County Museum, 1953–1954; Marlborough Fine Art (London), 1954, 1958 and [with Van Gogh] 1962; Saint-Jeoire-en-Faucigny, 1957; National Gallery, Belgrade, 1959; Musée du Louvre, 1963–1964 [BIBLIOGRAPHY 17].

Chief among paintings not in this exhibition are Sill Life, 1883 (National Gallery, Berlin); The Milliners, 1885–1886 (Bührle Collection, Zürich); View of Collioure, 1887 (The Lehman Collection, New York); Le Dimanche Parisien, 1888–1890 (Private collection, Paris); Cassis, Cap Canaille, 1889 (Jerome Hill, New York); Fishing Boats at Sunset, 1891 (Mr. and Mrs. John Hay Whitney, New York); Sailboats in the Harbor at Saint-Tropez, 1893 (Von der Heydt Museum, Wuppertal); The Red Buoy, 1895 (estate of P. Hébert, Paris); Mont-Saint-Michel, Fog, 1897 (Private collection, Zürich); The Yellow Sail, Venice, 1904 (Georges Besson, Paris); The Red Towers of La Rochelle, 1913 (Folkwang Museum, Essen).

Bibliography: See BIBLIOGRAPHY 1, 3, 4, 5, 6, 8, 9, 11, 14, 15, 17, 18, 20, 22, 23, 24, 26, 27, 28, 29, and Françoise Cachin, "Paul Signac" in BIBLIOGRAPHY 2; Georges Besson, Paul Signac, Paris, 1935, and Signac Dessins, Paris, 1950, also Signac, Paris, 1950; Lucie Cousturier, Signac, Paris, 1922; Félix Fénéon, "Signac", Les Hommes d'Aujourd'hui, vol. 8, no. 373, 1890, and "Paul Signac", La Plume, vol. 3, no. 57, 1 September 1891, pp. 292–299; John Rewald, The History of Impressionism, Museum of Modern Art, 1946 et seq.; Signac (J. Rewald, ed.), "Extraits du journal inédit [. . .]", Gazette des Beaux-Arts, vol. 6, no. 36, 1949 to no. 42, 1953, and "Le Néo-Impressionnisme, Documents", Gazette des Beaux-Arts, vol. 6, no. 12, 1934, pp. 49–59, also "Charles Henry", Cahiers de l'Etoile, vol. 8, January – February 1930, p. 72, and Jongkind, Paris, 1927.

90

GAS TANKS AT CLICHY (LES GAZOMETRES A CLICHY).
1886.
Oil on canvas, 25 1/2 × 31 7/8" (64.8 × 81 cm.).
Signed and dated l.l. "P. Signac 86".

Early exhibitions: Paris, "8e Exposition de Peinture" [last
Impressionist exhibition], 15 May – 15 June 1886, no. 188;
Paris, Indépendants, 21 August – 21 September 1886,
no. 365 ("Mars – Avril 1886").

Collection National Gallery of Victoria, Melbourne

For several years Signac had painted Impressionist landscapes
in strong colors and impetuous brushwork. In the months
just before the last Impressionist exhibition of May, 1886, he
adopted Seurat's more rigorous technique and color theory
in paintings like this one, shown in the May exhibition. The
center of the picture is dominated by the opposition of
orange-red and blue, but the sky and foreground have little
in the way of contrasts, and the brushstroke retains
considerable softness and variety.

Van Gogh was much impressed by Signac when they met,
and he may have been inspired by this picture or one like it
when he painted factories seen across a meadow [formerly

W. Weinberg], once in the collection of Père Tanguy,—whom Signac had known already in 1883. Signac's social consciousness was vested in his life-long adherence to Anarchist-Communism, parallel to Van Gogh's religious convictions. Industrial subjects appropriate to such views were frequent in his work in the middle 1880s, as they were in the paintings of Dubois-Pillet, Angrand, Luce and Lucien Pissarro at exactly the same time, and in the drawings of Seurat. In their concern for modern urban life, the Neo-Impressionists and their friends among the Symbolists found a point of contrast with the older Impressionists, whom they regarded as middle-class conservatives.

This painting has sometimes been confused with a very similar one of the same date, *Passage du Puits Bertin* [Private collection, England], partly because Fénéon inverted the titles of the two in his review of the 1886 exhibition [BIBLIOGRAPHY 5]:

■ M. Paul Signac is attracted by suburban landscapes. Those of his paintings dating from this year are painted in divided tones; they attain a frenetic intensity of light: *Les gazomètres à Clichy* (mars – avril 1886) and *Le*

■ *Passage du Puits-Bertin à Clichy* (mars – avril 1886), with its palisades where work trousers and jackets are drying, with the desolation of its flayed walls, its scorched grass and its incandescent roofs in an atmosphere which asserts itself and darkens as it mounts upward, hollowing out an abyss of blinding blue [. . .]

91

PASSAGE DU PUITS BERTIN, CLICHY. 1886.
Ink, 9 1/2 × 14 3/8″ (24.2 × 36.5 cm.).
Signed l.l. "P. Signac".

Collection The Metropolitan Museum of Art,
Harris Brisbane Dick Fund, 1948.

This drawing has the same composition as the oil of the same title, the pendant to the previous picture. Its origins are in a conté crayon drawing signed "Clichy 86" [Private collection, Paris], probably the basis of the painting. The present drawing may have been proposed for publication but found unsuitable because of the fineness of the dots in brown and black ink. At least one guesses as much, for another drawing [Private collection, Paris], with larger and fewer dots of black ink, was the version actually reproduced in *La Vie Moderne* on February 12, 1887, as an "Impressionist drawing" with the above title. Camille Pissarro [no. 49] did not publish his dotted ink drawings, but Dubois-Pillet had three in *La Vie Moderne* in 1887 and 1888, and Seurat had one in April, 1888, the standing *Model* of the oil painting [no. 81]. It may have been during this brief flurry of interest in such drawings that Seurat copied [estate of C. M. de Hauke] a section from Charles Blanc's *Grammar of the Arts of Design* on stipple engraving, in which the writer stresses the antiquity of the process and its appropriateness "for interpreting light and color". *La Vie Moderne* was the host for other drawings in a more conventional manner, reproducing three by Luce, two each by Seurat, Signac and Hayet, one each by Cross and Van Rysselberghe, and a great many by Lucien Pissarro, all in the years 1887–1888.

92
LES ANDELYS (LA BERGE, PETIT ANDELY). 1886.
Oil on canvas, 25 1/2 × 32″ (65 × 81 cm.).
Signed and dated l.r. "P. Signac 86".

Early exhibition: Paris, Indépendants, 26 March − 3 May
1887, no. 450 ("La Berge [Petit Andely]. Août 1886").

Private collection, Paris.

Daubigny's views of Bonnières established this kind of
composition thirty years earlier, but Signac has stressed the
homely aspects of the buildings in strong oranges and blues,
with a feeling for the contemporary and the ordinary that the
Barbizon generation would have considered perverse.
Compared with paintings of the preceding spring [no. 90],
this landscape has a more uniform brushwork and greater
variety of hue.

93

BREAKFAST (LE PETIT DEJEUNER). 1886–1887.
Oil on canvas, 35 × 45 1/4" (89 × 115 cm.).
Signed and dated l.l. "86 P. Signac 87" and l.r. "Op. 152".

Early exhibitions: Paris, Indépendants, 26 March – 3 May
1887, no. 449 ("La Salle à Manger"); Brussels, Les XX,
February 1888, no. 1; Paris, Hôtel Brébant, "Exposition des
peintres Néo-Impressionnistes," 2 December 1892 –
8 January 1893, no. 66.

Collection Rijksmuseum Kröller-Müller, Otterlo.

Signac was always a landscapist, and exclusively so after
1896, but he did several ambitious figure compositions,
including the *Milliners* of 1885–1886, *Le Dimanche Parisien*
of 1888–1890, and the portrait of Fénéon [no. 98]. *Breakfast*
has some of the hieratic feeling of Seurat's *Parade*, and
shares his ambition to create stable and permanent forms,
but it comes from a different tradition, recalling Pissarro,
Monet and Impressionist interiors, British paintings of the
mid-century, and Dutch genre. The distinctive palette of
oranges, purples and blues is Signac's own, and was later
of great influence in Belgium, where Van Rysselberghe and
Lemmen adopted it for interior portraits. One of the most
remarkable features of the picture is the isolation of the
elements on the table and the prominence of their counter-
shapes, emphasized by the use of color opposites. Gauguin
introduced similar effects in his paintings in 1888, and so
did Matisse in his *Dinner Table* of 1897 and *Harmony in Red*
of 1908–1909.

A dotted drawing [The Lehman Collection, New York] of
Breakfast was published in *La Vie Moderne* on April 9, 1887.

94
QUAY AT CLICHY. 1887.
Oil on canvas, 18 1/4 × 25 3/4" (46 × 65 cm.).
Signed and dated l.l. "P. Signac 87" and l.r. "Op. 157".

Early exhibitions: Brussels, Les XX, February 1888, no. 4;
Paris, Indépendants, 22 March – 3 May 1888, no. 624
("Op. 157. Clichy. Avril – Mai 1887").

Formerly S. Bing.
Collection The Baltimore Museum of Art,
Gift of Frederick H. Gottlieb.

Van Gogh also painted at Clichy the same year, and in a
manner close to this Signac. The Clichy view has a less
integrated brushwork than the Andelys picture of the
previous summer [no. 92]. The dabs come forward on the
surface, and are rather widely spaced, somewhat like
Gausson's and the Pissarros' canvases of 1886. It is possible
that the unusual graphism of the painting, the deep
perspective and the controlled impetuosity are a temporary
reassertion of his pre-1886 style under the impact of
associating with Van Gogh. On the other hand, there is a
drawing signed "Clichy 1886" [Private collection, Paris] of
much the same site, and perhaps the oil was largely done
that year, and touched up in 1887.

95

THE HARBOR OF PORTRIEUX (PORTRIEUX, LE PORT).
1888.

Oil on canvas, 24 × 36 1/4" (61 × 92 cm.).
Signed and dated l.l. "Signac 88" and l.r. "Op. 190".

Early exhibitions: Paris, Indépendants, 3 September –
3 October 1889, no. 245 ("Sept. 88"); Brussels, Les XX,
February 1890, no. 7.

Collection Staatsgalerie Stuttgart.

The stark simplicity of the composition has no real precedents. Many painters, including Jongkind, Courbet and
Monet had shown the sea at right angles, but with little of
the insistent regularity of Signac. Seurat's paintings at
Honfleur in 1886 provide the nearest example and
undoubtedly encouraged Signac to go further. Mondrian
later [no. 174] will build upon Neo-Impressionist seascapes
until finally his "plus and minus" paintings will bring the sea
forward as pure rhythm.

Signac was vacationing with Jean Ajalbert, the Symbolist
poet, when he began this picture. The Symbolists were
especially attracted to Signac's and Seurat's seascapes, even
those, like Huysmans, who could not appreciate their figure

compositions. Ajalbert himself was fond of the mesmerizing
calm of the sea. "It is raining", he wrote Signac in 1887
[Signac archives], "the water is dirty, there's a thick haze,
but it is the sea, and I could spend my life looking at it,
stupidly, like a peasant watching his cows at pasture, and
that is enough, and there is only that, and I think that I am
swallowing infinity which unfolds beyond the waves and the
horizon line". The "opus" numbers Signac had begun using
in 1887 are another clue to his friendships with the
Symbolists, for they evoke the music which underlay
Symbolist theory and which formed a meeting ground
between painters and poets. Because music can be expressed
in mathematical terms—the scale can be derived by the
regular subdivision of a given length of resonating string,
octave equalling one-half, and so forth—the number theories
which attracted Seurat and Signac usually involved
discussions of music. Three years after the Portrieux
campaign, Signac subtitled his seascapes "adagio" and
"presto". Mlle. de Forges' remark about one of those
[BIBLIOGRAPHY 17] could be applied to this picture: the
horizontal lines and the regular placement of the small boats
evoke the tablature and notes of musical writing.

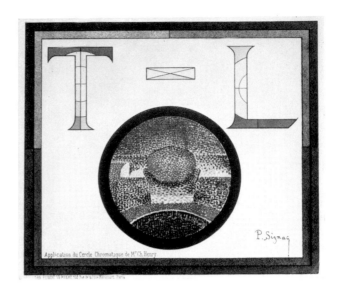

96

APPLICATION DU CERCLE CHROMATIQUE DE
MR. CH. HENRY. 1888–1889.
Color lithograph, 6 3/8 × 7 3/8″ (16.2 × 18.7 cm.).

Collection Museum of Fine Arts, Boston,
Gift of Peter A. Wick, 1955.

The color lithograph was originally designed to call attention
simultaneously to Charles Henry's book *Le Cercle Chromatique* (for which Signac also made a poster in watercolors),
and to the Théâtre-Libre, hence the "T-L". The union of both
was appropriate, because Henry was intimately involved in
Symbolist publications, and the Théâtre-Libre was the
theater in which Signac's friend Alexis had his play produced,
La Fin de Lucie Pellegrin. Seurat and Signac provided
drawings for the review of the play in *La Vie Moderne*
[June 17, 1888]. In its present form, the lithographs was
adapted in 1889 as a program cover for another play at the
same theater, *La Reine Fiammette* by Catulle Mendès; the
program is printed on the verso.

More wit than science entered into the colors of the
lithograph, but they provide lessons in Henry's color theory
and also in the general theory of contrasting colors. Starting
at the bottom of the right side of the "Γ", rising up to the

top and down the other side, one has the colors in the order
Henry placed them on his wheel. The "L" repeats the first
portion of this sequence, but upside-down. In the tondo,
the hair of the spectator turns bluish-green to oppose the
orange-red of the stage; the central portion of his hair is
purple, and therefore flanked by the yellow of the footlights,
the base of his hair again becomes bluish-green as it meets
the ruddy flesh tones of his neck. The outside border pairs
color opposites and then echoes them in reversed order
across the square. In the lower left, the outside is dark green
next to the red inner band; in the opposite corner, the outer
band is dark red and the inside, green.

97

CASSIS, CAP LOMBARD (COTE D'AZUR). 1889.
Oil on canvas, 26 × 31 7/8" (66 × 81 cm.).
Signed and dated l.l. "P. Signac 89" and l.r. "Op. 196".

Early exhibitions: Brussels, Les XX, February 1890, no. 9;
Paris, Indépendants, 20 March – 27 April 1890, no. 739.

Formerly Charles Storm; Dr. W. J. H. Leuring.
Collection Gemeentemuseum, The Hague.

The orange rocks show strongly against the blue water, but
the large expanse of tan cliffs and sand, and the sky, subdue
this contrast and produce a lightness that approaches
Seurat's harmonies of the same year [no. 87]. Fénéon
mentioned this picture in 1890 [BIBLIOGRAPHY 5] when he
praised Signac for dominating nature, using terms that
embody the prevailing anti-Impressionism of the Neo-
Impressionist circles:

■ M. Paul Signac has been able to create exemplary
specimens of an art of great decorative development,
which sacrifices anecdote to arabesque, nomenclature
to synthesis, fugitive to permanent and [. . .] confers on
Nature, which finally grew tired of its precarious reality,
an authentic Reality.

99

PLACE DES LICES, SAINT-TROPEZ. 1893.
Oil on canvas, 25 3/4 × 32 1/8" (65.4 × 81.5 cm.).
Signed and dated l.r. "93 P. Signac" and l.l. "Op. 242".

Early exhibitions: Brussels, La Libre Esthétique, February
1894, no. 400 ("Les Platanes"); Paris, Indépendants,
9 April – 26 May 1895, no. 1406 ("Les platanes, St. Tropez").

Formerly E. Raudag; Raphaël Gérard; Marcel Kapffer.
Collection Museum of Art, Carnegie Institute, Pittsburgh.

The same ancient plane-trees are still at Saint-Tropez, a quiet
fishing village when Signac first came to it in 1892. The color
is not yet as strong as that of a decade later, but one sees
already the rich contrasts that Cross will build upon, and
which Signac will develop further. In the foliage above, the
large dots swirl about and change direction more according
to the surface pattern than to any movement of leaves and
branches in reality. Naturalism is flouted in other ways, too.
Signac still claimed at this date that natural laws of light
dictated the colors, but he let the laws develop themselves
with little reference to everyday vision. The tree trunks of the
middleground, surrounded by foliage, acquire violet tones
because the adjacent yellow projects onto them its color

opposite; the red is there as the opposite of the neighboring
green.

100
UMBRELLA PINE (LE PIN PARASOL) "AUX CANOUBIERS".
1897.
Oil on canvas, 25 1/2 × 31 7/8" (65 × 81 cm.).
Signed l.r. "P. Signac 1897".

Formerly Berthe Signac.
Musée de l'Annonciade, Saint-Tropez

The composition is less exciting than the previous picture,
but the greens, purples, oranges, lavenders and pinks provide
an even richer foreground. Around the principal tree, the
ground is a strong orange, as though the tree's growth
heated up the earth. In his journal on August 9, 1897
["Journal inédit", see above], Signac writes of this picture
and the degree to which its elements are invented, rather
than seen.

■   For this landscape I act as I would for a large studio
    painting, fixing in advance my subject and my com-
    position, and then going out to find in nature the
    necessary information. I am very happy with this
    method, and I will no longer use any other. In working
    here [Saint-Tropez, in his studio] I see what little
    importance and what little use that working directly

■ after nature has [. . .]. I am sure that the man who is
   really strong can make everything come entirely out of
   his head.

The effect of the sky against which I place this big pine
cannot be seen from the Canoubiers. Should I therefore
deprive myself of it, of this large mass of yellow which
brings into relief the somber mass of the pine?

104

VENICE, ENTREE DU GRAND CANAL. 1905.
Oil on canvas, 29 × 36 1/4" (73.5 × 92 cm.).
Signed and dated l.r. "P. Signac 1905".

Early exhibition: Paris, Bernheim-Jeune, 21 January –
2 February 1907, no. 12 ("Entrée du Grand Canal").

Formerly O. Loury, J. J. Rumtz
Collection The Toledo Museum of Art, Toledo, Ohio.
Gift of Edward Drumond Libbey.

Saint-Tropez entered the history of art only in 1892 when
Signac first went there, but Venice belongs to the history of
many centuries. In the period 1895–1905, it is seen more
through the eyes of the British than through her own
painters Titian or Giorgione. Cross and Signac were not the
only ones to interest themselves in Ruskin, Turner and
Venice. Translations of Ruskin's *Stones of Venice* were
published in Paris in 1905, the year of this painting, and
1906. Ruskin generally was much appreciated, and Proust,
after writing articles on him in 1900, began to publish
translations of his writings in 1904.

In a letter to Angrand [Angrand archives] of February 3,

1904, Cross had spoken for himself and for Signac when he
commented on Venice and Saint-Tropez:

■ The admiration and the taste one has for the coast of
   Provence is an excellent preparation for the sensual joys
   of Venice. Their beauties, so different, are reunited in an
   equal amiability: the one is rough and exposed, the
   other is light and decorated with the most precious
   jewels. And, as in "Sacred and Profane Love" by Titian,
   they look at their reflections in the same water.

105
RAILROAD BRIDGE (PONT DE LA GARE). 1925.
Watercolor, 10 3/8 × 16" (26.3 × 40.6 cm.).
Signed and dated l.l. "P. Signac 1925".

The Lehman Collection, New York.

106
STILL LIFE WITH FRUIT. 1926.
Watercolor, 11 3/4 × 16 1/2" (30 × 42 cm.).
Signed and dated l.l. "14 Juillet 1926 P. Signac".

Collection Mr. and Mrs. Jack E. Butler, New York.

147

Emile Bernard
(1868–1941)

109
LA PLACE SAINT-BRIAC. c. 1887.
Oil on canvas, 18 1/8 × 21 5/8" (46 × 55 cm.).
Signed l.l. "Emile Bernard".

Collection O. Centner, Paris.

Like most of the artists who eventually grouped themselves
around Gauguin, Bernard passed through a phase of Neo-
Impressionism, in which he used divided colors and a
structured brushwork. This seems to have been from the
summer of 1886 into the next summer, and perhaps into the
winter of 1887–1888, but Bernard destroyed much of his
work of this period, and the chronology of his early style is
not yet clarified. The painting below is of the Breton port of
Saint-Briac, not far from Saint-Malo. Bernard is known to
have been there in 1888 and 1889, but it seems most likely
that this picture would have been done in 1887.

Henri Delavallée
(1862–1943)

110
FARMYARD (COUR DE FERME). 1887.
Oil on canvas, 23 1/2 × 28 3/4" (59.7 × 73 cm.).
Signed and dated l.r. "H. Delavallée 87".

Formerly Delavallée family; Private collection, Quimper.
Collection Paul Josefowitz, Switzerland.

Jules-Henri Delavallée is the least known of all French
artists in the present exhibition, but he has considerable
merit. He was at Pont-Aven in 1886, and met Gauguin then,
and he also knew Camille Pissarro, though only slightly. He
showed with the Indépendants in 1888, listing his address
as Marlotte (south of Paris, near the Fontainebleau forest),
but his two pictures *Effect of Snow* and *Flowering Thyme*
were not noticed by contemporary critics. He apparently put
Neo-Impressionism aside in the 1890s, but returned to it
after 1900, following several years of travel in Turkey.

111
ROADWAY IN THE SUN (LA RUE EN SOLEIL). c. 1907.
Oil on canvas, 18 × 22" (45.7 × 56 cm.).
Signed l.l. "Delavallée".

Collection Mr. and Mrs. W. J. Holliday, Indianapolis, Indiana.

Maurice Denis
(1870–1943)

112

GIRL IN A RED DRESS. 1894.
Oil on cardboard, 11 1/4 × 14 1/2" (28.5 × 37 cm.).
Monogram l.r. "MAUD".

Collection Nina Josefowitz, Switzerland.

There are two periods when Denis drew close to the Neo-
Impressionists. The first is 1890–1891, when he did a
number of paintings fully in the Neo-Impressionist manner,
including two versions of *Mystère Catholique* (Jean-François
Denis, and the Rijksmuseum Kröller-Müller, Otterlo) of 1890
and 1891, and *Two Young Girls by the Lamp* (Dominique
Denis) of 1891 also. The second period was about
1904–1906, from which *Odysseus and Calypso* (The Art
Gallery of Ateneum, Helsinki) of 1905 is a leading example.
Like the Fauves, he was then a frequent visitor to Signac and
Cross in Provence, and often used their large, mosaic-like
brushstrokes.

This charming little picture above is not, truly speaking, a
Neo-Impressionist work, but is typical of the many paintings
in which Denis, Vuillard and others of the Nabis group built
upon the decorative possibilities of the Neo-Impressionist
texture. Using the color-opposites red and green, Denis

places large dabs over the surface in a spirit more like that of
Cubist still-lifes twenty years later.

153

Paul Gauguin
(1848–1903)

113
STILL LIFE WITH HORSE'S HEAD (NATURE MORTE A LA
TETE DE CHEVAL). c. 1886?
Oil on canvas, 19 1/4 × 15″ (49 × 38 cm.).
Signed l.r. "Paul Gauguin".

Formerly Hjalmar Gabrielson; S. Lindquist.
Private collection, Paris.

Usually dated 1885, this painting might well be of the
following year instead. The divided color and uniform small
dabs are more readily assimilated with the work of Signac,
Seurat and the Pissarros from the spring of 1886 onward.
Gauguin met the younger artists some time before May, 1886,
when they were together at the last Impressionist exhibition,
and some of his Breton landscapes of the following months
have evident signs of the Neo-Impressionist technique.
Palette and brushwork of the still life suit this period more
than they do any of his pictures dated 1885. Gauguin's later
Neo-Impressionist still life *Ripipoint* (collection unknown) is
probably misunderstood today. Although the title is a
mocking one, only a serious and knowing application could
have produced such an integral structure.

Georges Lacombe
(1868–1916)

114
THE FOREST AT ALENÇON (CHENES ET MYRTILS, FORET
D'ALENÇON). 1895?
Oil on canvas, 18 × 24″ (45.7 × 61 cm.).
Monogram l.l. "GL".
Inscribed on stretcher verso: "Chênes et Myrtils (Forêt
d'Alençon). Epoque 1895".

Formerly collection Boutson.
Collection Mr. and Mrs. W. J. Holliday, Indianapolis, Indiana.

Lacombe is known only as a sculptor of the Nabis group,
but he was also a painter. Like most of the Nabis, he seems
to have flirted with Neo-Impressionism in the early 1890s,
and he also painted a good many pictures in divided color
and brushwork later. This was especially in the period
1905–1908, when Signac, Cross and the Fauves brought
about a second flowering of Neo-Impressionism, and when
Lacombe was a good friend of Van Rysselberghe. Mme. Mora-
Lacombe, the artist's daughter, believes that this picture
comes from the later period. The inscription on the stretcher,
however, would seem consistent with the palette and
practice of other painters of the 1890s, and in the very year
1895, Lacombe exhibited several paintings at the Indépendants.

Claude Monet
(1840–1926)

115
BOATS AT ARGENTEUIL. 1874.
Oil on canvas, 23 × 31" (58.5 × 78.7 cm.).
Signed l.r. "Claude Monet".

Private collection, New York.

Monet's two paintings provide an opportunity to make direct comparisons with Neo-Impressionist works. The early painting, done twelve years before the birth of Neo-Impressionism, has a choppy, even-textured stroke for both water and land. From any distance, these areas give an effect similar to that of Seurat's early paintings [nos. 68–71], and to those of many of his fellow artists. The historical lineage of the chopped-straw brushwork includes Jongkind, from whom Monet learned much, and the Barbizon artists Rousseau and Diaz. Monet used the separate strokes to break color into related elements, but he did not incorporate the use of opposites. Grass and tree leaves have yellows and yellow-greens for light areas, blue-greens and blues for dark. A typical Neo-Impressionist painting of the same subject would have these, but also more pure orange in the lights and more pale blue in the darks, plus some reds and purples—and the sky would have nearly the same texture as water and land, not true of Monet's painting.

116

A BEND IN THE EPTE RIVER, NEAR GIVERNY (UN TOURNEMENT DE L'EPTE PRES GIVERNY). 1888.
Oil on canvas, 29 1/8 × 36 1/2" (74 × 92.7 cm.).
Signed and dated l.r. "Claude Monet 88".

Formerly William L. Elkins.
Lent by the Commissioners of Fairmont Park,
William L. Elkins Collection, Courtesy of the Philadelphia Museum of Art.

Monet's later painting has a variety of brushstroke that seems to approximate the "real" qualities of natural foliage, and hence appears so different from the arbitrariness of contemporary Neo-Impressionist surfaces (its color, too, is quite different). This is the embodiment of the "romantic personality" which Félix Fénéon, Gustave Kahn and other Symbolist critics disapproved of, preferring the neutral brushwork of Neo-Impressionism because it better fitted their concept of permanence and monumentality of form.

Monet's texture, however, compared with landscapes of the middle of the century, is itself very arbitrary and does not really look like leaves. It is equally a formula, but the formula incorporates a significant shifting of size, type and direction of the individual dabs of pigment. Pictures like this, or *Poplars at Giverny, Sunrise* (Museum of Modern Art, New York) of 1888, with their large areas of tapestry texture, give rise to the question of whether or not they represent Monet's reaction to Neo-Impressionism. It seems likely, because other signs are found in his series of poplar trees (1888–1891) whose simple horizontals and verticals recall Seurat's compositions. Of course these tendencies were in Monet's earlier work, but they were undoubtedly brought to a head by the advent of Neo-Impressionism.

Roderick O'Conor

(1860–1940)

117

STILL-LIFE WITH BOTTLES. 1892.
Oil on canvas, 21 3/4 × 18 1/4" (55.2 × 46.3 cm.).
Signed and dated u.l. "R. O'Conor 92".

Collection The Trustees of The Tate Gallery, London.

O'Conor was an Irishman who spent most of his life in France, after early studies in London and Antwerp. He associated with the Nabis group in Brittany and in Paris, and knew Gauguin as well as the others. His still-life cannot properly be called a Neo-Impressionist work, yet it incorporates its divided color and broken brushwork, together with echoes of Van Gogh, a combination that will later be common in Germany and the Lowlands. Van Gogh and Neo-Impressionism came together in the work of Henry Van de Velde, Jan Thorn-Prikker, Curt Herrmann, and Jawlensky, to name a few.

Vincent Van Gogh
(1853–1890)

118
A CORNER IN THE PARK (COIN DE PARC; PARC
MONTSOURIS). 1886.
Oil on canvas, 23 3/8 × 32" (59.3 × 81.2 cm.).
De la Faille catalogue 353.

Formerly V. W. Van Gogh; Private collection, Scotland;
Henry R. Luce.
Collection Yale University Art Gallery, New Haven, Connecticut.
Gift of Mr. and Mrs. Henry R. Luce.

Neo-Impressionist color and divided brushwork had a
profound impact on Van Gogh. He knew Signac, Angrand,
Gausson and Lucien Pissarro well, and both Camille Pissarro
and Seurat slightly. This painting of 1886 is among
Van Gogh's first essays in Neo-Impressionism. It is not based
upon the use of divided color, nor even upon the Neo-
Impressionist palette. It shows instead the attraction that the
regular brushwork of the new style had for so many artists
of the time. The trees are in various greens, with some
yellow and blue, and the foreground also is essentially in
local colors rather than in opposites. In 1887, when he
sometimes worked with Signac, Van Gogh changed to the
much hotter colors of the Neo-Impressionists, and he
produced a number of pictures in which color-opposites are

used forcefully (the *Self Portrait* in the Art Institute of
Chicago, or the *Interior of a Restaurant* in the Rijksmuseum
Kröller-Müller). After he went to Arles in early 1888,
Van Gogh no longer painted in the small strokes of the 1887
period, but he retained the use of opposites "à la Seurat",
as he wrote of his *Bedroom at Arles* (Art Institute of
Chicago), and his long and energetic streaks of pigment are
often interlaced according to Neo-Impressionist principles.

Alfred William Finch
(1854–1930)

Finch, called "Willi" or "Willy" by his friends, was born in
Belgium of British parents in 1854, and should be regarded
essentially as a Belgian artist. He visited England periodically,
and his wife and children bore English names, but little yet is
known of his ties with his parents' homeland. He studied at
the Brussels Academy from 1878 to 1880, at the same time
as his friend James Ensor. They were both among the
founders of Les XX in 1884. Finch also knew Whistler,
perhaps through visits to England, and had him invited to
the first exhibition of Les XX (Whistler, in turn, invited Finch
to successive exhibitions of The Royal British Artists in
London, in the winters of 1887 and 1888). Finch's work in
the Neo-Impressionist manner began in the winter of
1887–1888, following the exhibition of Seurat's and Camille
Pissarro's paintings at Les XX in February, 1887, and the
constantly growing contacts with Paris. In January 1888, he
wrote Octave Maus (secretary of Les XX) of his fear that his
work would too closely resemble that of "our friends in
Paris", and he volunteered a dotted drawing for the catalogue
of the February exhibition [letter and drawing, see
BIBLIOGRAPHY 26]. Paintings exhibited that year included
several of Suffolk, England, but these antedated his adoption
of the new style. The height of his Neo-Impressionist activity
was reached in the period 1890–1892, after which his
paintings drop sharply off. By 1890 he was attached to the
Boch pottery works at La Louvière and remained there until
1892, increasingly concerned with ceramics. He experimented
with Neo-Impressionist color theory in pottery glazes, and
wrote Maus that he had designed some plates using Charles
Henry's theories of harmonic proportions. With Georges
Lemmen, who seems to have been his most intimate friend,
he visited England in 1892, then he settled in Brussels for
several years. Few paintings are dated after 1892 until his
later removal to Finland, and it is known that he had his own
kiln for his ceramics. It can now be proved, furthermore, that
he worked with Henri Van de Velde at Uccle and that his
pottery was chosen to represent the Uccle establishment in
1897 [Van de Velde archives].

Count Louis Sparre, a Swedish painter, met Finch in 1897
and lured him to the Iris pottery works at Borgå, Finland.
Although he intended to stay but a year, Finch spent the rest
of his life in Finland, with occasional visits to Paris, Germany,
Italy and England. By May 1899, the Borgå arts and crafts
center began to founder—according to Finch [Van de Velde
archives]—owing to Count Sparre's frivolity and to the fact
that every commercial order had to pass through the hands
of the historian Julius Meier-Graefe, appointed sole agent
for the Continent. Finch was named teacher of ceramics at

the Central School of Industrial Arts in Helsinki in 1902, and he entered prominently into the art life of the capital. In November, 1903, he wrote Van de Velde of the "Exhibition of French and Belgian Painters" that he was organizing for the coming year, to include Seurat, Signac, Cross, Van Rysselberghe and Lemmen, as well as Monet, Degas, Pissarro, Renoir, Denis, Vuillard, Bonnard and others. It was the first exhibition in Finland of Impressionist works, and had an immediate effect. Rallying around Finch and the critic and architect Sigurd Frosterus, young artists began to develop the modern Finnish school. In 1908 Finch helped form the Septem Group, which began exhibiting in 1912 and continued until 1928. Of the original group (Enckell, Ollila, Oinonen, Rissanen, Thesleff, Thomé), only Werner Thomé seems to have painted in the Neo-Impressionist fashion. In the opening exhibition of 1912, his and Finch's divisionist works were noted, and Finch's early paintings were preferred by the critics to his current, softened style. Although he sometimes used large, free dabs of paint, his paintings after 1900 are usually in a quasi-Impressionist style rather like Luce's. His role in this century was found more in his ceramics, furniture and other industrial arts, and his collaboration with Saarinen and others to establish modern art in Finland. As a Neo-Impressionist, he was most significant from 1889 to 1892, and his paintings of those years are of truly superior quality.

Finch has seldom been included in exhibitions devoted to Neo-Impressionism, partly because of the scarcity of his works. As a founding member of Les XX, he exhibited paintings from the beginning in 1884, until 1893. He showed paintings with the Indépendants in Paris only once, in 1890 (in 1891 he sent ceramics there). Thereafter his occasional participation in exhibitions in France and Germany was limited to ceramics. In Helsinki, he exhibited paintings regularly with the Septem Group from 1912 through 1928.

His important Neo-Impressionist pictures include *The Race Course at Ostende*, 1888 (Art Gallery of Ateneum, Helsinki); *La Route de Nieuport*, 1889–1890 (Private collection, Mariehamn, Finland); *Orchard at La Louvière*, 1890–1891 (Art Gallery of Ateneum); *Rocks, Dover*, 1892 (Private collection, Helsinki); *August Moon*, 1898 (Art Gallery of Ateneum).

Bibliography: See BIBLIOGRAPHY 1, 2, 4, 14, 23, 25, 26, 27, and Bertel Hintze, "A. W. Finch, Peintre Néo-Impressionniste", *Ateneumin Taidemuseo Museojulkaisu.* vol. 11, nos. 1–2, 1966, pp. 8–15, 39–42 [valuable, but errors in captions and some dates incorrect]; Sakari Saarikivi, "The Septem Group and Finnish Impressionism", *Art in Finland* (Alf Krohn, ed.), Helsinki, 1953, pp. 49–58; Salme Sarajas-Korte, "Le Peintre Belge A. W. Finch", *Finlandia* [Special issue for Brussels Fair], 1958, pp. 50–52; R. Sihtola, "A. W. Finch [. . .]", *Suomen Taiteen Vuosikirja* (L. Wenner-virta and Y. Jäntti, eds.), Helsinki, 1945.

120
HAYSTACKS (LES MEULES). 1889.
Oil on canvas, 12 1/2 × 19 3/4″ (32 × 50 cm.).
Signed and dated verso "A. W. Finch 89".

Early exhibitions: Brussels, Les XX, February 1890, no. 2;
Paris, Indépendants, 20 March − 27 April 1890, no. 355.

Formerly Octave Maus.
Collection Musée d'Ixelles, Brussels

Almost all of Finch's paintings were done along the Channel
coast or just inland from it, and he was faithful to its moist,
grey light. The thinly covered canvas has related hues that
give an overall greyness, except for the juxtaposition of blue
and orange for the rooftops and the shadows of the
haystacks. The identical composition, but in the form of a
small study [Mr. and Mrs. Hugo Perls, New York], was
painted by Georges Lemmen, who must have stood beside
Finch when he began his canvas.

121

BREAKWATER AT HEYST, GREY WEATHER (L'ESTACADE
A HEYST, TEMPS GRIS). 1889–1890.

Oil on canvas, 14 1/8 × 21 1/4" (36 × 54 cm.).
Signed l.l. "A. W. Finch".

Early exhibitions: Brussels, Les XX, February 1890, no. 4
("L'Estacade à Heyst; temps gris"); Paris, Indépendants,
20 March – 27 April 1890, no. 357 ("Un brise lames
à Heyst, temps gris, Novembre").

Formerly Private collection, Brussels.
Collection Mr. and Mrs. Hugo Perls, New York.

The radical simplicity of this superb seascape shows Finch
carrying one aspect of French Neo-Impressionism to a
further point. Seurat's *Honfleur, Evening* [no. 79], which
Finch saw at the exhibition of Les XX in 1887, has wooden
pilings also, but they are attached to the shore and follow
its slope, creating a more traditional space. Signac's
Portrieux seascapes [no. 95] of 1888 are closer to Finch, but
the closest of all are Seurat's of Gravelines. These, however,
were painted in the summer of 1890, after Finch's, and the
conclusion that we must draw is that the Belgian painter
built upon Seurat's and Signac's early seascape style

towards one of his own. Henry Van de Velde had shown his
Blankenberghe beach scene [no. 140] at Les XX in 1889,
another case of a composition stripped down to fewer
elements than in any French pictures of the same time.

In addition to the impulsion towards geometric simplicity
that Parisian Neo-Impressionism began, there was also its
concern for subtle light effects, here merging with the earlier
current of Impressionism. The dense, even light that Finch
created in his painting follows upon works exhibited at
Les XX in 1889 by Seurat and Pissarro. Seurat showed *Banks
of the Seine, Grey Weather* [collection now unknown], and
Pissarro sent a painting of fog over the Seine [John G. Johnson
Collection, Philadelphia] and another subtitled "hoar frost".
The subsequent identification of Neo-Impressionism with the
hot palettes of Signac and Cross in the Fauve period makes
it something of a surprise to see how common were blond
and grey effects in the early work.

122
BOATS ON THE SHORE [LE CHENAL DE NIEUPORT,
TEMPS GRIS, ETE]. 1889–1890.
Oil on canvas, 25 3/4 × 31 7/8″ (65.5 × 81 cm.).
Signed and dated l.r. "AW. Finch 1890".
Border painted by Finch.

Early exhibitions: Probably Brussels, Les XX, February 1890,
no. 1 ("Le Chenal de Nieuport, temps gris, été"); Probably
Paris, Indépendants, 20 March – 27 April 1890, no. 304 ("Le
Chenal de Nieuport, temps gris, été; app. à Mme. Simon").

Formerly "Mme. Simon"?
Collection Mrs. Clara Ekholm, Helsinki.

Finch's composition probably owes a debt to Seurat's
Fishing Fleet at Port-en-Bessin [Museum of Modern Art,
New York], exhibited at Les XX in 1889, but the prominent
boats are strong patches on the surface that form abrupt
rhythmic contrasts which Seurat seldom used. The painted
border, which Lemmen also adopted in 1890, comes directly
from the French artist.

123
BREAKING WAVES AT HEYST. 1891.
Oil on canvas, 26 1/4 × 35 3/4″ (66.5 × 91 cm.).
Signed and dated l.l. ″A. W. Finch 1891″.

Formerly Sigurd Frosterus.
Collection Mrs. Johanna Weckman, Helsinki.

124
ENGLISH COAST AT DOVER [LES FALAISES AU SOUTH
FORELAND]. 1891–1892.
Oil on canvas, 26 1/8 × 31 5/8″ (66.5 × 80.5 cm.).
Signed and dated l.r. "1892 AW. Finch".
Border painted by Finch.

Early exhibition: Probably Brussels, Les XX, February 1892,
no. 1 ("Les Falaises au South Foreland").

Collection Ateneumin Taidemuseo,
(The Art Gallery of Ateneum), Helsinki.

Finch had the habit of dating his works on the eve of their
completion for the February exhibitions of Les XX, therefore
this painting must have been begun in 1891. A trip to the
Dover coast was very simple from the Belgian shore, and
Finch's English ancestry might have encouraged him to make
these counter-images of his Heyst seascapes. He showed
three views of the English coast at Les XX in 1892, *The
Cliffs at South Foreland*, *The Pebble Beach at Dover*, and
The Warren near Dover, study. The second has disappeared,
but the third is apparently the one now called *Rocks, Dover*,
in a private collection, Helsinki. It is small (16″ wide) and
has the unfinished appearance of a study.

Georges Lemmen
(1865–1916)

Lemmen was born in Brussels in 1865 and died there in 1916, the only one of the Belgian Neo-Impressionists who remained in his homeland. The son of an architect, his formal training seems to have been less important than that he received at home; for a time he attended a drawing school at Saint-Joose-ten-Node. His early work shows the impact of Ensor's paintings of the early 1880s, and of Whistler. After being made a member of Les XX in late 1888, he was won over to Neo-Impressionism, and exhibited both with Les XX and with the Indépendants in Paris from 1889 through 1892, when he was grouped with the Neo-Impressionists. 1890 is the first year of a consistent use of divided brushwork and color, and the largest number of his best works are dated from 1892 to 1895. Over the last half of the decade he rapidly modified his style so that Neo-Impressionist elements disappear by the end of the century. Meantime, his role in the arts and crafts movement in Belgium was a central one, and was signaled by his articles on Walter Crane in 1891. He gave a large share of his time to printmaking and illustration, and also designed tapestries and other applied arts. For Les XX and its successor, La Libre Esthétique, he made posters, catalogue covers and title pages, and did the same for the review *L'Art Moderne*, to which he also contributed articles. Among his many collaborations with other artists, one might cite his illustrations for poems by Gustave Kahn and the typeface he created for Henry Van de Velde's edition of Nietzsche's *Also sprach Zarathustra* (Leipzig, 1908). He was a founding member of the group *L'Art*, which was established in 1894 to propagate the industrial and decorative arts. It included his close friend A. W. Finch, by then largely a ceramist, as well as Van Rysselberghe and the writers Emile Verhaeren, Edmond Picard and Octave Maus, who ran *L'Art Moderne*. Perhaps it was through Finch that Lemmen was aware of the arts and crafts movement in England; his articles of 1891 show detailed knowledge of Crane's activities. Family records document two trips Lemmen took to England, one in 1892, when he writes of Finch being with him, and the second in 1894.

After Lemmen turned away from Neo-Impressionism, he drew closer to Vuillard and "intimiste" painting, a notable difference being in the rather somber palette he maintained. He joined *Vie et Lumière*, established in 1904, a conservative group including the older Claus and Heymans, and this was a confirmation of the native current of value-conscious (rather than color-conscious) painting he practiced in his youth. His essay in *L'Art Moderne* of the same year, however, asserts the hegemony of French painting over Belgian, and is the work of an intelligent man who was no chauvinist.

Lemmen's etchings, lithographs and monotypes are now coming to be appreciated, and it is generally agreed than his drawings are his best work.

Lemmen exhibited both with the Indépendants and Les XX from 1889 through 1892, and thereafter quite regularly with La Libre Esthétique in Brussels. He has always been included in exhibitions of Belgian painting of the period, but only occasionally in those devoted to Neo-Impressionism. Druet gave him one-man shows in 1906 and 1908, and Giroux (Brussels) in 1913 and 1929. He had another one-man exhibition, at André Maurice in 1959. In 1965 his drawings and prints were shown at the Bibliothèque Royale de Belgique, and both paintings and drawings were in the modest retrospective at the Galerie de l'Institut in 1966.

Neo-Impressionist paintings by Lemmen include *Haystacks and Houses*, 1889 (Mr. and Mrs. Hugo Perls, New York); *The Merry-Go-Round*, 1890–1892 (Mme. Thevenin-Lemmen, Toulon); *Maisons à la Hulpe*, 1890 (Mr. and Mrs. Arthur G. Altschul, New York); *Heyst*, c. 1892 (Art market, London); *Factories on the Bank of the Thames*, 1892 (Rijksmuseum Kröller-Müller, Otterlo); *Two Sisters*, 1894 (Art market, London); *Mme. Georges Lemmen*, 1895 (Mme. Thevenin-Lemmen, Toulon).

Bibliography: See BIBLIOGRAPHY 1, 2, 4, 14, 23, 24, 25, 26 and Marcel Nyns, *Georges Lemmen*, Antwerp, 1954; J. F. Elslander, *Figures et Souvenirs d'une Belle Epoque*, Brussels, 1950; Georges Lemmen, "Walter Crane", *L'Art Moderne*, vol. 11, nos. 9 and 11, March 1891, pp. 67–69 and 83–86, and "Propos d'Actualité", *L'Art Moderne*, vol. 24, no. 10, 6 March 1904, pp. 73–75; Octave Maus, *L'Art et la Vie en Belgique*, Brussels, 1921; Louis Piérard, *La Peinture Belge Contemporaine*, Paris, 1928; Henri Thevenin, catalogue of the exhibition, Galerie de l'Institut, 1966.

125

UNDERNEATH THE LAMP (SOUS LA LAMPE). 1890.
Crayon, 18 7/8 × 17" (48 × 43 cm.).
Dated l.l. "jeudi 12 juin 90.", and l.r. "19 juil. 90.", and
stamped l.r. "GL".

Collection M. and Mme. Pierre Lemmen, Brussels.

Represented are the artist's mother and grandmother, to the
rear, and his father and sister Julie in the foreground. The
style recalls both Van Rysselberghe [no. 133] and Seurat.
Unsigned drawings by Lemmen have been attributed to
Seurat, and it is true that he owned a Seurat drawing (*Clair
de Lune*), but their styles are easily distinguished.

126
PORTRAIT OF JULIE LEMMEN, THE ARTIST'S SISTER.
1891.
Oil on canvas, 24 1/2 × 20 1/2" (62.2 × 52 cm.).

Early exhibition: The Hague, Kunstkring, "Tentoonstilling van Schilderijen en teekeningen van eenigen uit de 'XX' en uit de 'Association pour l'Art'", July 1892, no. 16.

Collection The Art Institute of Chicago, A. A. McKay Fund.

Like Van Rysselberghe in his portraits, Lemmen retains the specific qualities of his sitters' features, with a homely directness that is often disconcerting. It was quite conscious, as can be shown by comparison with his painting of the same subject two years earlier (Marcel Nyns, Brussels). In the earlier portrait, his sister appears as an elegant *mondaine*, seated in the same pose. She is dressed in outdoor clothing, and behind her the room has several active planes and still-life elements. Her face is generalized and made symmetrical, deliberately "pretty". In the Neo-Impressionist portrait, all accessories are drastically simplified, and the artist makes clear that he was seeking the directness of vision of Holbein and masters of the Northern Renaissance. That this comes in part from Seurat is probable, for Lemmen contributed to the Indépendants in 1890, where Seurat had his similar portrait of Signac [no. 88] and his *Woman Powdering Herself* [Courtauld Collection].

127
HEYST AT NIGHTTIME (HEYST LA NUIT). c. 1891.
Oil on wood, 4 3/4 × 8″ (12 × 20.3 cm.).

Collection Joan and Lester Avnet, Kings Point, New York.

128
MADAME LEMMEN SEATED. 1892.
Crayon, 13 1/2 × 9 3/4" (34.2 × 25 cm.).
Stamped l.r. "PL".

Formerly M. and Mme. Pierre Lemmen.
Collection Mr. and Mrs. Hugo Perls, New York.

131
SEACOAST (LA MER). 1893.
Charcoal, 9 1/2 × 12 1/4" (24 × 31 cm.).
Dated l.c. "2 Juin 93" and stamped "GL".

Collection Mme. Thevenin-Lemmen, Toulon-Mourillon, France.

Like many of his figure studies [no. 128] and his prints,
Lemmen's handsome seascape has qualities of the Art
Nouveau. Such drawings are consistently his best work, and
have something of Edvard Munch about them.

173

129
STUDY FOR "THAMES SCENE, THE ELEVATOR" (LA
TAMISE). 1892.
Oil on wood, 6 1/4 × 9 1/2" (16 × 24 cm.).
Stamped l.r. "GL".

Collection Mme. Thevenin-Lemmen, Toulon-Mourillon, France.

Lemmen did a great many of these beautiful panels from
about 1889 to 1894. The night scene [no. 127] has little
besides the direct contrast of orange and blue, but this study
has oranges, pinks, reds, violets, blues, greens and some
yellow. Oranges and blues, the archetypal Neo-Impressionist
pair, continue to provide the principal oppositions.

132

SUNDAY /

Oil on canv

Signed and

and title ve

Collection

Morren wa

Sunday in

the Indéper

standing at

stirring an

at all resem

unconsciou

and the cha

to the conte

similar [no.

[Rijksmuse

feeling. The

stove. Its dr

Color is one

attractive pi

center; abov

130

THAMES SCENE, THE ELEVATOR (LA TAMISE). 1892.
Oil on canvas, 24 × 33 3/4" (61 × 86.7 cm.).

Formerly Linje Collection.
Collection Museum of Art, Rhode Island School of Design,
Providence.

This is Lemmen's masterpiece, and a comparison of its colors
with those of the preceding study is both a pleasure and a
basic lesson in Neo-Impressionism. Precedents for the
composition can be readily found in Dubois-Pillet [no. 27]
and Pissarro [no. 48], but their colors are far simpler.

Landscape did not form as large a part of Lemmen's work as
figure painting, but he often turned to outdoor subjects in
the summer. The Thames picture must have been done in his
studio, after returning from his first trip to England in 1892.
He was there again in 1894 (and wrote to his family about
a boat trip he and his bride took down the Thames), but the
palette seems to indicate the earlier year.

Geor
(1868

Morre
partly
destro
born c
died a
deposi
Antwe
period
record
annual
contrib
made l
by the
comple
of flow
colorat
exhibit
that "h
this, hi
of pain
decora
activity
exhibiti
and he
War. A
and he
1902 a
the gro
belong
Saint-(
in the l
was giv
and 19
and 19
marked
Neo-Im
althoug
a softer

Bibliog
receivec
et de Li
Morren,
Sirène e
"Exposi
p. 149,
1893, p
16 Dec(
the Bru:

Théo Van Rysselberghe
(1862–1926)

Van Rysselberghe, long regarded as the principal Belgian Neo-Impressionist, was born in 1862, the last of five sons of a well-to-do building contracter in Ghent. He studied at the Academy there, then for a short time at the Brussels Academy. When only nineteen, in 1881, he won a travelling fellowship on the strength of the two pictures he showed in the Brussels Salon. He went to Spain with the Hispano-Belgian painter Dario de Regoyos (later a Neo-Impressionist for a short period), and in 1883 to Morocco. These were the first of many trips which took him all over eastern and western Europe, as well as North Africa and the Near East, by the end of the century. As a founding member of Les XX in 1884, and already an intimate friend of Octave Maus, its secretary, and the poet Emile Verhaeren, Van Rysselberghe began to play a major part in the introduction to Belgium of avant-garde French and English art. For all the significance of Ensor and others of the group, Van Rysselberghe was second only to Maus in forming the taste of the exhibition society and its successor (from 1894), La Libre Esthétique. In 1887, for example, he visited Toulouse-Lautrec in Paris and urged him upon Les XX, long before the French artist was known; in 1889, in a single letter to Maus from Paris, he records efforts to enlist Gausson, Hayet, Van Gogh, Lautrec, Dubois-Pillet, Degas, Gauguin and Filliger, either visiting them in person or attending their exhibitions.

Van Rysselberghe's early style shows an admiration for Manet, Degas, Hals, the Spanish masters, Whistler (whom he met in 1885), and Ensor of the early 1880s, not as eclectic a combination as it might seem, for they had in common a loose but strong brushwork and a love of contrasting light effects that was the mark of much progressive painting of the period in Belgium. The fact that they were all portraitists is equally significant, because Van Rysselberghe remained one all his life. His earliest important Neo-Impressionist paintings were in 1888, two years after his first contact with Seurat and Signac, and only in 1889 did he turn over completely to the new style. By then he was thoroughly immersed in the art circles of Paris, as well as Brussels, and along with Signac and Verhaeren, was among the chief emissaries linking the two cities. For a time in the middle 1890s, he designed furniture and the applied arts (some in collaboration with Henry Van de Velde), and he was a major illustrator of books by Verhaeren and other writers. He also designed posters, catalogues and the actual installations for Les XX and La Libre Esthétique, but in essence he was a painter. His work of the early 1890s is largely portraits and landscapes. From 1895 to 1898 he had a crisis of self-doubt and did much less painting. In the latter year he moved to Paris, and began to confirm changes that were already noticeable: he turned increasingly to the female nude, to large decorative paintings of the human figure out-of-doors, and to a loosened and modified Neo-Impressionist brushwork. This essentially conservative streak steadily broadened, until by about 1908 he had left Neo-Impressionism behind. His close friendship with Signac had waned by the turn of the century, but he remained intimate with Cross until his death in 1910, and he joined both of them in contributing to the development of Fauvism. It was apparently he who got the Fauves to exhibit regularly in Brussels with La Libre Esthétique from 1906 on. Most of his later life was spent in Paris and on the Mediterranean coast, where he died in 1926.

Paul Fierens, Van Rysselberghe's admirer and biographer, said simply that "he lacked imagination". Van Rysselberghe's strength and his weakness lay in the same qualities: He never forsook a rather traditional concept of chiaroscuro (he did grisaille drawings right through his Neo-Impressionist period) and he did not, as did Cross and Signac, give first place to the construction of color harmonies in the dialogue between picture and nature. Instead, he gave it to the subject *qua* subject, without always making a proper balance with creativity. One should be content, however, with such a large number of paintings in which directness of vision and a love of light formed what Maurice Denis called "an art of probity and reflection, with neither hesitations nor maladroitness, a realistic art, but with all the seductions of reality".

Exhibitions of Neo-Impressionism have always included Van Rysselberghe, and from the late 1890s to the first World War he was usually included in major international exhibitions of contemporary art. As a leader of Les XX and La Libre Esthétique he was in most of their annuals, and in 1898 and 1904 was given virtual one-man shows by the latter group. In Paris, he contributed to the Indépendants from 1890 to 1895, and from 1901 to 1906. His first one-man exhibition was at Laffitte in Paris, in 1895, and thereafter, at the Maison des Artistes in 1902, Druet in 1905, Bernheim-Jeune in 1908, Giroux (Brussels) in 1922 and 1927, Braun in 1932 and the Musée des Beaux-Arts, Ghent, in 1962.

Van Rysselberghe's principal early painting is his portrait of Octave Maus of 1885 (Musées Royaux des Beaux-Arts, Brussels). Among Neo-Impressionist paintings, one might cite the *Portrait of Alice Sèthe*, 1888 (Willy Du Bois, Brussels); *La Petite Denise*, 1889 (Counard-Cuypers, Rixensart); *Tennis Game*, 1890 (Pierre Fauré, Toulouse); *Portrait of Maria Sèthe*, 1891 (Musée Royal des Beaux-Arts,

Antwerp); *The Harbor at Cette*, 1892 (Mr. and Mrs. John Hay Whitney, New York); *Portrait of Irma Sèthe Playing the Violin*, 1894 (Mr. and Mrs. Hugo Perls, New York); *Windmill in Flanders*, 1894 (Mr. and Mrs. Hugo Perls); *Seascape*, 1894 (Gemeentemuseum, The Hague, conditional gift); *Portrait of Paul Signac "En Bateau"*, 1896–1897 (Ginette Signac, Paris); *La Lecture au Jardin*, 1902–1903 (Wittamer-De Camps, Ancien Hôtel Solvay, Brussels); *La Lecture*, 1903 (Musée des Beaux-Arts, Ghent); *Pines at Cavalière*, 1904 (Rijksmuseum Kröller-Müller, Otterlo).

Bibliography: See BIBLIOGRAPHY 1, 2, 4, 13, 14, 15, 18, 20, 22, 23, 24, 26, 27, 28, 29, and M. J. Chartrain-Hebbelinck, "Théo Van Rysselberghe", *Revue Belge d'Archéologie et d'Histoire de l'Art*, vol. 34, nos. 1–2, 1965, pp. 99–134, and (with P. Mertens), "Lettres de Théo Van Rysselberghe à Octave Maus", *Bulletin des Musées Royaux des Beaux-Arts de Belgique*, vol. 15, nos. 1–2, 1966, pp. 55–112; Maurice Denis, catalogue of the Giroux exhibition of 1927; Paul Eeckhout and G. Chabot, catalogue of the Ghent exhibition of 1962; Paul Fierens, *Théo Van Rysselberghe*, Brussels, 1937; François Maret [i.e., Franz van Ermengen], *Théo Van Rysselberghe*, Antwerp, 1948; Guy Pogu, *Théo Van Rysselberghe* [brochure, privately printed; contains serious errors], Paris, 1963; Maria Saint-Clair [i.e., Van Rysselberghe], *Galerie Privée*, Paris, 1947.

133
EVENING, THE THREE SETHE DAUGHTERS (INTERIEUR,
LE SOIR, LES TROIS FILLES SETHE). 1889.
Conté crayon with touches of gouache, 19 1/2 × 25 1/4″
(49.5 × 64 cm.).
Monogram and date l.r. "TVR 1889".

Formerly Octave Maus; Madeleine Octave Maus.
Collection Mr. and Mrs. Hugo Perls, New York.

Van Rysselberghe's vision is that of a painter who, although
thinking in black and white, is careful to preserve a
modulation of light appropriate to the fluidity of pigment.
In nearly the same subject [no. 125], Georges Lemmen
instead reveals the opposite vision, that of the draftsman who
exploits the dry, rubbed texture of crayon, which then he will
transcribe into paint.

134

A CRAG NEAR ROSCOFF IN BRITTANY (LA POINTE PER-KIRIDEC). 1889.
Oil on canvas, 26 3/4 × 41 3/4″ (68 × 106 cm.).
Monogram and date l.r. "18 TVR 89".

Early exhibitions: Brussels, Les XX, February 1890, no. 5 or no. 6; Brussels, Les XX, February 1891, no. 1; Paris, Indépendants, 20 March — 27 April 1891, no. 1214; Krefeld, "Ausstellung Flämischer Künstler", 1898, no. 118.

Formerly Max Klinger.
Collection Rijksmuseum Kröller-Müller, Otterlo.

Van Rysselberghe was much in Paris in 1889 before he went to Brittany in October, and he would have seen Signac's paintings of the Breton harbor of Portrieux [no. 95] at the Indépendants, as well as those of Cassis in Signac's studio. In this first full year of his Neo-Impressionism, his seascapes are closer to Signac than to Seurat. Even so, direct comparisons show how different he and Signac really were. Signac, in his Cassis painting [no. 97], places us at a greater distance from the water, and at the same time creates on the surface those arbitrary and planar shapes of beach, water and sky against which his rocks appear as abstract crystals of giant size. Van Rysselberghe's rocks, so near to us, actually seem smaller in absolute scale, and we are not presented with that statement of separate, ordered parts which Signac provides. The Belgian painter wanted us to have a feeling of real rocks being covered by real water, something Signac cheerfully ignores.

142
WOMAN AT THE WINDOW (FEMME A LA FENETRE).
1889.
Oil on canvas, 43 3/4 × 49 1/4" (111 × 125 cm.).
Billéter-Hammacher catalogue 20.

Early exhibitions: Brussels, Les XX, February 1890, no. 1;
Paris, Indépendants, 20 March – 27 April 1890, no. 816
("Faits du Village. VI. La Femme assise à la Fenêtre");
Antwerp, "Als ik kan", November 1891, no. 261; Munich,
"Münchener Jahres-Ausstellung vom Kunstwerk aller
Nation", 1893, no. 1584 ("Frau am Fenster").

Formerly A. J. Heymans.
Collection Koninklijk Museum voor Schone Kunsten, Antwerp,
Belgium.

The subject is a traditional one in the Lowlands, but one
feels that Van de Velde wanted to rival both Millet and
Seurat, the two French artists he most admired. It is as though
he were "correcting" his countryman Henri de Braekeleer
(1840–1888) by taking one of his favored subjects and

recasting it in a Neo-Impressionist mold. Unlike the earlier
Bath House at Blankenberghe, this painting uses the color-
opposites associated with pigments rather than with natural
light. The greens of the house walls outdoors increase, for
example, as they approach the pink street.

The exhibition in Munich of 1893 has not previously been
noted. Van de Velde also showed there nos. 1585 and 1586,
"Im Bluthenmonat" and "Germinal". For the previous picture,
the Hague exhibition of 1892 has not been recorded, either.
It would seem that Van de Velde's paintings had a larger role
in these years than has been thought.

NEO–IMPRESSIONISM IN HOLLAND

André Derain
(1880–1954)

155

BIG BEN. 1905.

Oil on canvas, 31 1/8 × 38 5/8″ (79 × 98 cm.).

Signed l.l. "a derain".

Collection Pierre Lévy, Troyes, France.

Like Matisse, Derain incorporated into his art the primary impulses from the Post-Impressionists Van Gogh, Cézanne, Gauguin and the Nabis, and the Neo-Impressionists. It was their intense color and expressive drawing which first attracted the Fauves in the period before 1908. Derain's major Neo-Impressionist paintings were done in 1905 under the impact of Matisse with whom he spent the summer at Collioure (Matisse, in turn, had been at Saint-Tropez with Signac the previous summer). His *Big Ben* has a freer version of the mosaic brushwork of Signac and Cross, and an organization of architecture and water which is commonly found in their paintings. The orange sun and its reflection are alike decomposed into orange, yellow and red. In the sky, the sun pulsates in the midst of an intense assortment of blue strokes, which give way to green towards the horizon. On the water, blue and green flank the reflection of the sun, acting as local color and as opposites of the orange and red. In other paintings, Derain carried the juxtaposition of

opposites even further, and proved himself a closer student of Neo-Impressionist color theory than was Matisse of the same period. However, both Van Gogh and Monet are recalled by this picture, and it would be unwise to isolate the Neo-Impressionist current from the energetic amalgam that was then taking place in Derain's art.

Curt Herrmann
(1854–1929)

Curt Herrmann was born on February 2, 1854, in Merseburg and died in Pretzfeld on September 13, 1929. He grew up in Halle and Berlin, studying in Berlin with Franz Steffeck and in Munich with W. Lindenschmidt. At first a conservative portraitist, he became progressively more alert to new currents. His first contact with Neo-Impressionism began in 1897, when he and his wife acted as hosts to Henry Van de Velde and Constantin Meunier in Berlin. He knew Count Kessler and Julius Meier-Graefe well, and probably his first Neo-Impressionist paintings date from the winter of 1898–1899, following the late autumn exhibition of Neo-Impressionism which Kessler organized in Berlin. The German review *Pan* had also published lengthy excerpts from Signac's *D'Eugène Delacroix au Néo-Impressionnisme* in 1898, and five years later, having visited Signac in Paris, Herrmann's wife published an integral German translation of the entire book. Herrmann, meantime, had helped found the Berlin *Secession*, and also joined in the establishment of the Deutsche Künstlerbund. From 1902 to about 1910, his contacts with Paris were frequent, and he organized a Neo-Impressionist section in the Berlin Secession in 1906. He, Van de Velde, Meier-Graefe and Kessler were the ones most responsible for the Germans' interest in Neo-Impressionism. He corresponded with Fénéon, Signac, Cross, and Van Rysselberghe whom he visited in France, and often saw Van de Velde. He and his wife accompanied the Belgian artist on a trip through the Near East in 1903. Like Kessler and Meier-Graefe, Herrmann purchased pictures by the Neo-Impressionists, and he also commissioned a portrait of his wife by Bonnard.

Herrmann first exhibited in 1891, at the Internationale Kunst-Ausstellung in Berlin; he showed with the first Berlin Secession in 1899, and regularly thereafter; he also contributed to various exhibitions in major German cities from the late 1890s to the first World War, and to the Indépendants in 1905 and 1907. He was given a major retrospective at the National Gallery in Berlin in 1924, and modest but valuable one-man shows by Wolfgang Gurlitt, Munich, in 1954; the Ashmolean Museum, Oxford, in 1955; and Matthiesen, London, in 1956. Dr. W. Kramm and his colleagues of the city museum of Kassel will publish a catalogue of Herrmann's work at the time of their monumental exhibition in the summer of 1968, after having restored his paintings over a period of several years.

Bibliography: See BIBLIOGRAPHY 16, 23, 25, 27, and W. Gurlitt and H. Heilmaier, catalogue of the Munich exhibition of 1954; A. M. Hammacher, *Le Monde de Henry Van de Velde*, Antwerp, 1967; Curt Herrmann, *Der Kampf um den Stil*, Berlin, 1911; Henry Van de Velde (Hans Curjel, ed.), *Geschichte meines Lebens*, Munich, 1962. The artist's family preserves his important archives.

156

EARLY MORNING: THE OLD TIMBER BRIDGE, PRETZFELD   213
(MORGENSTIMMUNG; SOMMERMORGEN). 1902.
Oil on canvas, 27 1/2 × 39" (70 × 99 cm.).
Monogram l.c. "CH".

Early exhibitions: Probably Berlin, "Secession", 1902, no. 83
("Sommermorgen"); Probably Hamburg, Cassirer, "Ausstellung Deutscher und Französischer Neoimpressionisten",
January 1903 ("Sommermorgen"); Weimar, Deutsche und
Französische Impressionisten und Neo-Impressionisten",
summer 1903, no. 27 ("Schloss Pretzfeld") [This exhibition
apparently travelled also to Berlin].

Collection the Artist's family, England.

162
LANDSCAPE WITH FOUNTAIN. c. 1906–1907.
Oil on canvas, 21 × 29" (53.3 × 73.6 cm.).
Signed l.r. "J. Metzinger".

Lent by Margit Chanin, Ltd., New York.

Metzinger's Neo-Impressionist period was somewhat longer
than that of his close friend Delaunay. At the Indépendants
in 1905, his paintings were already regarded as in the Neo-
Impressionist tradition by contemporary critics, and he
apparently continued to paint in large mosaic strokes until
some time in 1908. The height of his Neo-Impressionist work
was in 1906 and 1907, when he and Delaunay did portraits
of each other (Art market, London, and Museum of Fine Arts,
Houston) in prominent rectangles of pigment. (In the sky of
the previous picture is the solar disk which Delaunay was
later to make into a personal emblem.) Metzinger's landscapes
of 1905–1906, mostly seacoast views, have relatively small
square strokes and fairly deep spaces, usually with receding
shorelines. By 1907, his work became more abstract and
quite literally like mosaics. In a brief statement he made at the
time, reprinted by George Desvallières in *La Grande Revue*
(vol. 124, 1907), he called upon parallels with literature

which twenty years before had been the hallmark of Neo-Impressionism and its alliance with the Symbolist writers.

■ I ask of divided brushwork not the objective rendering of light, but irridescences and certain aspects of color still foreign to painting. I make a kind of chromatic versification and for syllables I use strokes which, variable in quality, cannot differ in dimension without modifying the rhythm of a pictorial phraseology destined to translate the diverse emotions aroused by nature.

What Metzinger means is that each little tile of pigment has two lives: it exists as a plane whose mere size and direction are fundamental to the rhythm of the painting and, secondly, It also has color which can vary independently of size and placement. This is only a degree beyond the preoccupations of Signac and Cross, but an important one. Writing in 1906, Louis Chassevent recognized the difference (and as Daniel Robbins pointed out in his Gleizes catalogue, used the word "cube" which later would be taken up by Louis Vauxelles to baptize Cubism): "M. Metzinger is a mosaicist like M. Signac but he brings more precision to the cutting of his cubes of color which appear to have been made mechanically [. . .]". The interesting history of the word "cube" goes back at least to May 1901 when Jean Béral, reviewing Cross's work at the Indépendants in *Art et Littérature*, commented that he "uses a large and square pointillism, giving the impression of mosaic. One even wonders why the artist has not used cubes of solid matter diversely colored; they would make pretty revetments".

Giuseppe Pellizza da Volpedo
(1868–1907)

163
THE ROUND DANCE (GIROTONDO). c. 1902–1904.
Oil on canvas, circular, 39 3/8" (100 cm.) diameter.

Collection Civica Galleria d'Arte Moderna, Milan.

164

WASH DRYING IN THE SUN (PANNI AL SOLE). 1905.
Pastel and tempera on canvas, 33 × 50 3/4" (87 × 131 cm.).
Signed and dated l.r. "G. Pellizza 1905".

Formerly Ludovico Cartotti.
Lent by Gallerie d'arte Sacerdoti, Milan.

Pellizza da Volpedo is an exception among the Italian
Divisionisti because in certain pictures, of which this is the
best, he drew close to French Neo-Impressionism. Segantini,
Previati, Grubicy and the other Divisionists developed parallel
to Neo-Impressionism, but were independent of it. Like their
French counterparts, they grew from the generation of
Impressionists and like them, they were much concerned with
color theory. The Italians, however, were equally close to
Barbizon art, and in both subject matter and style maintained
ties with the middle of the nineteenth century.

Wash Drying in the Sun is a naively direct application of
Neo-Impressionist theory. Full sunlight eliminates most color
reactions and leaves only itself, hence the meadow is
mostly yellow, with some white for reconstituted light and
some orange for partly-absorbed light. In shade, the local

color green is allowed to come forth, and to it is added blue,
the opposite of orange, some purple, the opposite of yellow,
and some red, its own contrasting hue. The strongly
delineated shapes fortify the contrasts of hue and help give
the composition a French flavor. His other painting has a
rather dull palette by comparison, and its twilight vibration
of light is more typical of Italian Divisionism.

223

Christian Rohlfs
(1849–1938)

165
WEIMAR PARK, GARDEN ENTRANCE (WEIMARER PARK,
GARTENEINGANG). c. 1902.
Oil on canvas, 30 × 19″ (76.5 × 48.4 cm.).
Monogram l.r. "CR".

Formerly Becker collection.
Collection Städtisches Karl-Ernst-Osthaus Museum, Hagen.

Rohlfs was brought to Hagen in 1901 on the advice of
Henry Van de Velde, who had just completed the redesigning
of Karl Ernst Osthaus' museum and town house. The
Folkwang collection was there also, and both were rich in
French and Belgian Neo-Impressionism. Rohlfs fell under the
spell of Signac, Cross and Seurat, and in 1904 was still
referring to himself as a Neo-Impressionist. In that year,
however, he began to change again, this time towards the
expressionistic style for which he is best known. Paintings
dated as late as 1907, such as the *Birch Trees* now in Essen,
still have a mosaic-like structure, but energized by contact
with Van Gogh. Wilhelm Niemeyer [BIBLIOGRAPHY 16]
makes a convincing case for Rohlfs' position in the development of pure color from Neo-Impressionism to Kandinsky.

Louis Valtat
(1869–1952)

167
WOMAN A LA MODE. c. 1902–1904.   225
Oil on canvas, 12 5/8 × 10 5/8" (32 × 27 cm.).

Collection Mme. Ginette Signac, Paris.

166
L'OMNIBUS MADELEINE-BASTILLE. 1895.
Oil on canvas, 51 1/8 × 59 7/8″ (130 × 152 cm.).
Signed l.r. "L. Valtat".

Formerly A. Vollard.
Collection Modern Art Foundation, Oscar Ghez, Geneva.

Valtat combined something of the *intimisme* of his friends
Vuillard and Bonnard with the divided color and brushwork
of the Neo-Impressionists. Like K. X. Roussel, he stood
between the Nabis of the 1890s and the Fauves, a decade
later. The large street scene is of 1895, when he began to
use small strokes and opposing colors. Although the
technique and color come from Neo-Impressionism, he weds
them to an atmospheric suffusion of tone and dissolved contours to create an effect closer to Bonnard. The next picture is
typical of his later work, in which larger strokes are somewhat
more like the contemporary work of Signac and Cross. It is
one of three that were owned by Signac, and is another
indication of the close ties between Neo-Impressionism and
Fauvism.

THE CUBIST PERIOD AND AFTER

Giacomo Balla
(1878–1958)

168

GIRL RUNNING ON A BALCONY (BAMBINA CHE CORRE
SUL BALCONE). 1912.
Oil on canvas, 49 1/4 × 49 1/4″ (125 × 125 cm.).
Signed and dated l.r. "1912 Balla".
Archivi del Futurismo 37.

Collection Civica Galleria d'Arte Moderna, Milan.

Three different historical currents come together in this
painting, the most famous of several Balla did in a Neo-
Impressionist manner: movement and photography, Seurat's
late style, and Neo-Impressionist color and technique. Aaron
Scharf [*Burlington Magazine*, May 1962] and Joshua Taylor
[*Futurism*, 1961] have discussed the Futurists' enthusiasm
for stroboscopic photography, particularly that of Edward
Marey, as an expression of the dynamism of modern life.
Scharf believes Seurat may have been aware of Marey, but
whether this is so or not, his *Chahut* of 1888–1890 (Rijksmuseum Kröller-Müller, Otterlo) was particularly admired by
the Cubists and Futurists, and it had a numerous progeny in
the work of Metzinger, Villon, Lhote, Severini and others.
The repeated parallels of its dancers' legs and costumes, and
the stage footlights, created an insistent rhythmical beat that
appealed to the later artists. Movement was also related to
Impressionist and Neo-Impressionist color. The Futurist
Umberto Boccioni declared that by treating the atmosphere
between objects as a subject of attention, the French
painters had begun what the Futurists would consummate:
the interaction of objects with their environment. By 1912,
Balla was well versed in theories of light, color and motion.
Light and color had preoccupied him in his earlier days as
a Divisionist, and his *Street Light* of 1909 [Museum of
Modern Art, New York] is full of pulsating movement
generated by the quasi-abstract arrowheads of intense colors
that embody the decomposition of artificial light.

The bands around the edge of Balla's painting are undoubtedly derived from Seurat's painted borders and frames.

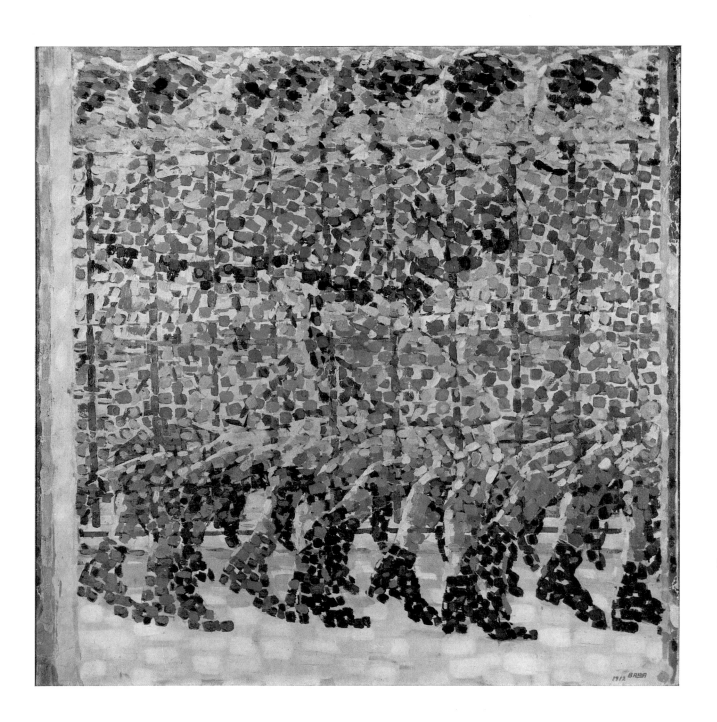

Georges Braque

(1882–1963)

169

CERET: THE ROOFTOPS (LA FENETRE, CERET). 1911.
Oil on canvas, 32 3/8 × 23 1/4″ (82.2 × 59 cm.).

Formerly Robert von Hirsch.
Collection Mr. and Mrs. Ralph F. Colin, New York.

Seurat and the Neo-Impressionists had a role in the development of Cubism, although a minor one compared with Cézanne's, and the presence of this and other Cubist works in the present exhibition might help define it. Seurat's drawings and the underlying structure of his paintings provided lessons in the adjustment of flat planes of geometric shape to an arbitrary pulsation of light and dark as two edges meet [*La Parade*, no. 82]. Signac's paintings [no. 95] have some of the same light-dark florescences and the skeletal geometry. In general, the predilection of the Neo-Impressionists was for an assertive geometry that appealed to the generation active in 1910–1914, both Cubists and Futurists. Braque, according to André Salmon [*L'Art Vivant*, 1920], had a reproduction of Seurat's *Chahut* on the wall of his studio before 1911, and its rhythms are found here in the Céret composition.

Is it possible also to relate the mosaic brushwork of Analytical Cubism to Neo-Impressionism? Delaunay, Metzinger and Severini used Neo-Impressionist brushwork, and Delaunay's was virtually monochromatic in 1910 and 1911. With Braque and Picasso, however, the absence of color makes the relationship more tenuous. Circumstantial evidence is there: the popularity of Neo-Impressionism since 1904 and the annual Indépendants exhibitions, Braque's own flirtation with Neo-Impressionism [no. 153], and the later appearance of mosaic color in Cubist paintings of 1913 and after. Perhaps equally convincing is the fact that the regular horizontal tiles of paint begin to appear in Braque and Picasso only in 1910, at the same time they are being used by Delaunay and others, and well after the early impact of Cézanne on their work.

Robert Delaunay
(1885–1941)

170

WINDOW ON THE CITY, NUMBER 4 (FENETRE SUR LA   231
VILLE). 1910–1911.
Oil on canvas, 44 3/4 × 51 1/2″ (113.7 × 130.8 cm.).
Signed and dated l.r. "r delaunay 1910–11".

Collection The Solomon R. Guggenheim Museum, New York.

One of the major landmarks in the history of Cubism was the
famous "Room 41" or "Cubist room" of the Indépendants in
1911, where this painting was shown. In 1910 and 1911
Delaunay did a number of paintings of patchwork texture,
and in some cases the individual rectangles take on the
existence of separate planes. At this point, color theory is not
involved, and this painting has few zones of contrast. Its
subdued color offers a parallel with the contemporary
paintings of Braque [no. 169] and Picasso, which are nearly
monochromatic. The checkerboard brushwork has been
exploited for its own sake, and is not expressive of color
theory. In 1912 and 1913, in his "windows" and his "disks",
Delaunay returned to Neo-Impressionist color theory (he read
Signac and Henry on color, as well as Chevreul and Rood),
but he abandoned the mosaic brushwork. Instead, he
embodied the decomposition of natural light in dynamic
pinwheels of pure color areas.

Juan Gris
(1887–1927)

171
STILL LIFE. 1916.
Oil on canvas, 18 1/8 × 15″ (46 × 38 cm.).

Formerly Katherine S. Dreier.
Collection The Solomon R. Guggenheim Museum, New York.
Gift of Katherine S. Dreier Estate.

Gris, Picasso and Braque all introduced prominent areas of
dabbed brushstrokes into their paintings in 1914, when the
individual planes of Synthetic Cubism were commonly given
a uniform texture, rather than the chiaroscuro of 1911–1912.
They may have been inspired by Metzinger, Marcoussis and
members of the "Puteaux group" who had continued to use
mosaic and checkerboard brushwork through 1912 and 1913.
Gris and Picasso did not concern themselves with color
theory at all, and the dabs are instead a decorative homage
to Neo-Impressionism. Their automatic rhythm is sometimes
echoed by checkerboards or similar patterns based on
textiles. D. H. Kahnweiler [*Critique*, January – February 1947]
believes that the Neo-Impressionist facture also appealed to
the Cubists because it eliminated bravura and personal
brushwork—as Fénéon had noted—and therefore suited the
impersonal feeling of collage and flat plane.

Gris was conscious of being a spiritual heir of Seurat, but it
was Picasso who actually did some paintings in a Neo-
Impressionist technique. In 1917 in Barcelona and at
Montrouge he painted a portrait of his wife [Vilato collection,
Barcelona], a large painting after Le Nain [Artist's collection],
and several others.

Paul Klee
(1879–1940)

172

MOSAIC STUDY (MOSAIKSTUDIE). 1925. 233
Oil on paper over cardboard, 16 × 21 1/2″ (40.4 × 54.5 cm.).
Signed l.r. "Klee" and signed and dated u.r. "1925 R. null.
Mosaikstudie Klee".

Collection Berner Kunstmuseum, Paul Klee-Stiftung.

It would be tendentious to claim that Klee's mosaic pictures
of the 1920s are in the Neo-Impressionist tradition, but it
seems possible that his contact with Delaunay and French
Cubism before the first World War was an indirect link. In
any event, the small colored planes of Neo-Impressionism
take on a new and marvelous life in his compositions.

Marevna Vorobieff
(born 1892)

Marevna was born on February 14, 1892, in Cheboksary, Russia, the natural daughter of the Polish nobleman Stebelsky and a Russian mother. After studies in Tiflis and Moscow, she travelled to Italy in 1911, where she frequented the entourage of Maxim Gorki, who became her protector. In 1912 she went to Paris, and studied for a time at the Colarossi Academy and the Russian Academy, both very free and informal art schools despite their names. With the intercession of many Russian friends, she met Zadkine, Soutine, Ilya Ehrenbourg and Diego Rivera, as well as Picasso and most of the Cubists. She formed a union with Rivera, and their daughter Marika later became her favorite model.

Marevna's Neo-Impressionism evolved from her love of Cubism, and from the early 1920s until about 1943, she painted her distinctive oils and watercolors in small, separate strokes. The integrity of her style, which outlived the heyday of early Neo-Impressionism, is perhaps explained by the fact that she devoted herself naively and directly to it, without questioning its relationship to contemporary art, and also by the fact that she lived in relative isolation and rather complete poverty throughout the period. She lived successively in Paris, Holland, and southern France, before moving to England after World War II.

Marevna began exhibiting in 1913, at the Indépendants, but the first of a succession of little one-man shows was not until 1929, at the Galerie Quotidien in Paris. She then was given others in The Hague, by Audretch, in 1930 and 1936; in Paris, by Zborowski in 1936, Roux in 1942, Galerie Claude in 1953; in London by Lefèvre in 1952, and at the Pushkin Club in 1958.

Among her best pictures are *Marika with a Hairband*, 1931 (oil, Private collection, New York); *Nude Woman Seated*, 1931 (watercolor on canvas, Art market, New York); *Little Negro Girl*, 1937–1938 (oil, Artist's collection, London). Many of her paintings of the 1930s masquerade as works by Seurat, Angrand, Van Rysselberghe and others, a curious and regrettable homage to her art.

Bibliography: See the autobiography *Life in Two Worlds*, London, 1962, and these newspaper and journal reviews of her exhibitions: Gustave Kahn in *Mercure de France*, 15 June 1929, and *Le Quotidien*, 10 January 1936; G. Maire in *La Presse*, 25 January 1930; G. J. Gros in *Paris-Midi*, 10 January 1936; P. Descargues in *Les Lettres Françaises*, 2 July 1953; R. Domergue in *L'Information*, 27 June 1953; Maurice Sérullaz in *France Illustration*, August 1953; R. Smith in *La Revue Moderne*, August 1953; *The Times* (London), 27 November 1958.

173
THE MALAGASY WOMAN (LA MALGACHE AUX PIMENTS).
1942–1943.
Oil on millboard, 41 3/8 × 29 1/8" (105 × 74 cm.).
Signed l.r. "Marevna".

Formerly collection Aslangul.
Collection Modern Art Foundation, Oscar Ghez, Geneva.

Marevna was inspired by the pan-Mediterranean life of wartime Cannes when she painted this portrait of a woman from Madagascar who was a servant near her studio. Most of her portraits are simpler, even rather severe in structure, and have fewer contrasts of bright tones.

235

Piet Mondrian
(1872–1944)

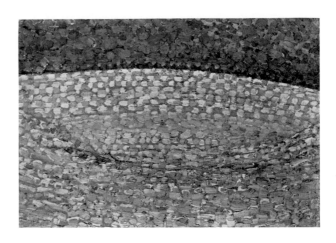

174
THE DUNES III (DUIN III). 1909.
Oil on cardboard, 11 5/8 × 15 3/8" (29.5 × 39 cm.).
Signed l.l. "P. Mondriaan".

Formerly S. B. Slijper.
Collection Gemeentemuseum, The Hague.

Mondrian's several paintings of dunes in his Neo-Impressionist period of 1909–1910 are a logical outgrowth of early Neo-Impressionism in the Lowlands, and foretell his most famous, mature work. Van de Velde, Finch and Toorop had all favored very simple expanses of beach, water and sky, and had carried such compositions to a simpler extreme than had Seurat or Signac. Mondrian grew up when Neo-Impressionism was one of the daring new styles being regularly exhibited, and he knew Toorop [no. 149], who was in Amsterdam before and during the 1909–1910 period. His use of the broad Neo-Impressionist strokes was a phenomenon common in Europe then, coming from Signac, Cross and the Fauves, and continuing into Cubism. Severini, Metzinger, and Delaunay were also using mosaic textures in 1909 and 1910.

The small plane as the basic building block of a surface was retained by Mondrian, until finally his great constructions of the 1920s came to consist of only a few large planes and bands.

Gino Severini
(1883–1966)

175

SPHERICAL EXPANSION OF CENTRIFUGAL LIGHT
(ESPANSIONE SFERICA DELLA LUCE CENTRIFUGA).
1913.
Oil on canvas, 24 3/8 × 19 3/4″ (62 × 50 cm.).
Signed l.r. "G. Severini".
Archivi del Futurismo 5C.

Collection Riccardo Jucker, Milan.

Severini was the closest of the Futurists to the tradition of
Neo-Impressionism, not the least because he lived so long
in Paris. He makes it clear in his autobiography that he
arrived in Paris in 1906 already full of admiration for Seurat,
and a large mosaic technique appears in his work by 1908.
His *Spherical Expansion of Centrifugal Light* is one of a large
group which grew from his paintings of dancers of 1912
which, in turn, had looked back to Seurat's *Chahut*. Severini
was an assiduous reader of Signac's treatise on Neo-
Impressionist color theory, and wrote that Seurat's art and
Signac's book were the founding supports of his art. Here he
has created a simple color relationship, going from hot colors
in the center to cool ones at the edges. Within any one zone,
color is varied only with related hues, but the whole is
built upon all the classical contrasts: yellow and purple,

orange and blue, red and green, with black and white for
good measure. Logically developed from his own earlier
work, these paintings probably also owed something to
Delaunay's "windows" and light discs, in which color is
broken into similarly abstract planes.

DOCUMENTATION

EXHIBITIONS
AND CHRONOLOGY

Note: The salient facts for individual artists are found in their biographies preceding the picture entries. All group exhibitions are listed here, but other principal events are recorded in diminishing density, according to their significance for Neo-Impressionism. Months of the year are listed only for the earliest events; Brussels exhibitions are given in detail only until 1895, after which they lost their vitality; exhibitions of the Indépendants are carried systematically only to 1906, since later they were less central to Neo-Impressionism; one-man shows and detailed chronology are not included after 1911. In the early exhibitions, the names of all Neo-Impressionists are mentioned, but other artists appear only as examples and are not systematically treated. Paris is understood as the city unless another is named, and the word "Gallery" has been omitted except when clarity required it.

1881 Seurat begins intensive study of color theory after release from military service. Publication of French edition of Ogden Rood's *Modern Chromatics*, which becomes fundamental treatise on color for Neo-Impressionists.

1882 Signac turns to painting full time, apprentices himself to Impressionist landscape.

1884 Brussels: In February, first exhibition of *Les XX*, founded previous year by Maus, Ensor, Finch, Van Rysselberghe and others. Invited guests include Rodin, Liebermann, Whistler, W. M. Chase and J. S. Sargent.

15 May – 1 July: "Salon des Artistes Indépendants" includes work by Angrand, Cavallo-Peduzzi, Cross, Dubois-Pillet, Redon, Schuffenecker, Seurat (*Une Baignade, Asnières*), Signac.

Most future Neo-Impressionists meet each other for first time at founding of this jury-free exhibition group. Irregularities provoke schism, and new society is organized with statutes written by Dubois-Pillet; their first exhibition is in December.

December: "Société des Artistes Indépendants" [hereafter called Indépendants]: Angrand, Bastien-Lepage, Cavallo-Peduzzi, Cross, Dubois-Pillet, Guillaumin, Schuffenecker, Seurat (landscape and panels for *Sunday Afternoon on the Island of the Grande Jatte*), Signac and others.

1885 Brussels: February, *Les XX:* includes Ensor, Finch, Toorop (new member), Van Rysselberghe. No contact yet with future Neo-Impressionists in Paris.

Publication of Charles Henry's *Une Esthétique Scientifique*, soon to become highly influential in Neo-Impressionist and Symbolist circles.

October: Seurat meets Pissarro, and close relationship is established among Seurat, Signac, Pissarro and his son Lucien over the next months. Seurat separates his colors with fine criss-cross and dotted brushstrokes, and introduces others to the latest theories of color.

1886 January–February: Pissarro exhibits in a dealer's shop window a small picture in divided color and dotted brushwork. March–April: Signac's first paintings in new style.

Brussels: In February, *Les XX* exhibition includes Ensor, Finch, Monet, Monticelli, Redon, Renoir, Van Rysselberghe, Whistler.

New York: Durand-Ruel exhibits the "Impressionists of Paris" in the spring, including Seurat (*Une Baignade, Asnières*), Signac and Pissarro.

May – June: Eighth and last Impressionist exhibition, with Degas, Gauguin, Seurat (*Sunday Afternoon on the Island of the Grande Jatte*), Signac (*Les Modistes*), Camille Pissarro, Lucien Pissarro, and others.

Seurat, Signac and the two Pissarros show paintings in small, regular brushstrokes; they win instant notoriety and consider themselves "scientific Impressionists" in opposition to Monet, Renoir and those they call "romantic Impressionists". Seurat and Signac meet the young scientist Charles Henry, whose writings on esthetics and color influence them profoundly.

20 August – 21 September: *Indépendants:* Angrand, Cavallo-Peduzzi, Cross, Dubois-Pillet, Lucien Pissarro, Redon, Henri Rousseau, Seurat (*Grande Jatte*), Signac.

Cavallo-Peduzzi and Dubois-Pillet now paint in the new technique, as do Gausson and Hayet (but these do not yet exhibit).

In a review of the *Indépendants* exhibition in the Belgian journal *L'Art Moderne*, Félix Fénéon first uses the term "Neo-Impressionism" and proclaims the new style as the successor to Impressionism.

Banquets, informal dinners and meetings offered by the *Indépendants* and *La Revue Indépendante* bring together the Neo-Impressionists and the Symbolist writers, who defend their friends' paintings in their reviews.

1887 Brussels: February, *Les XX:* Ensor, Finch, B. Morisot, Pissarro, Seurat (*Grande Jatte*), W. Sickert, Toorop, Van Rysselberghe.

Seurat's large picture causes sensation; friendships with Belgian painters and writers begin, and by end of year, Finch is painting in Neo-Impressionist technique.

26 March – 3 May: *Indépendants:* Angrand, Cavallo-Peduzzi, Cross, Dubois-Pillet, Gausson, Luce, Lucien

Pissarro, Redon, Rousseau, Seurat, Signac, and many others.

Angrand and Luce now exhibit Neo-Impressionist works, and French group is constituted this year except for Cross, only later a convert to the new style. Camille Pissarro does not exhibit with the *Indépendants*, but the others show in the same rooms together and dominate the exhibition society.

Van Gogh meets Signac, and paints many pictures in Neo-Impressionist technique. From late 1886 through this year, many of the artists around Gauguin, and that master himself, also try the new style.

1888 Brussels: February, *Les XX:* Anquetin, Dubois-Pillet, Guillaumin, Signac, Toorop, Toulouse-Lautrec, Van Rysselberghe, Whistler. [Present exhibition nos. 26, 93, 94.]

Signac and Dubois-Pillet represent the Neo-Impressionists at Brussels; Van Rysselberghe and Henry Van de Velde begin to paint in the new technique.

22 March – 3 May: *Indépendants:* Angrand, Anquetin, Cavallo-Peduzzi, Cross, Delavallée, Dubois-Pillet, Gausson, Luce, Lucien Pissarro, Rousseau, Seurat (*Poseuses, Parade*), Signac, Van Gogh. [Present exhibition nos. 3, 82, 84, 94 and probably 38 also.]

At offices of *La Revue Indépendante*, successive one-man shows through this year for Seurat, Signac, Dubois-Pillet, Luce and others.

Publication of Charles Henry's *Cercle Chromatique* for which Signac makes poster and advertising placard. Signac collaborates with Henry for about three years, making diagrams and plates for his lectures and writings on scientific theory.

1889 Brussels: February, *Les XX:* Cross, Lemmen (new member), Luce, Monet, Camille Pissarro, Seurat, P. Wilson Steer, Toorop, Van Rysselberghe, Van de Velde (new member). [Present exhibition nos. 38, 52, 84, 85, 140.]

Van Rysselberghe's first full year as Neo-Impressionist, and he is constantly in Paris as principal liaison with the French painters; Finch and Van de Velde major figures in Belgian group, and Lemmen begins to use divided color.

3 September – 4 October: *Indépendants:* Angrand, Anquetin, Cavallo-Peduzzi, Cross, Dubois-Pillet, Filliger, Gausson, Hayet, Lemmen, Luce, R. O'Conor, Lucien Pissarro, Rousseau, Seurat, Signac, Toulouse-Lautrec, Van Gogh. [Present exhibition nos. 87, 95.]

Camille Pissarro begins to modify his Neo-Impressionism.

1890 Brussels: February, *Les XX:* Cézanne, Dubois-Pillet, Finch, Hayet, Lemmen, Lucien Pissarro, Renoir, Segantini, Signac, Sisley, Toorop, Toulouse-Lautrec. Van Gogh, Van Rysselberghe, Van de Velde. [Present exhibition nos. 95, 97, 120, 121, 134. 142, and probably 122.]

Neo-Impressionism, with Lemmen now a member of the group, is the dominant new style in Belgium.

20 March – 17 April: *Indépendants:* Anquetin, Angrand, Cross, Dubois-Pillet, Filliger, Finch, Gausson, Guillaumin, Lemmen, Luce, O'Conor, Lucien Pissarro, Rousseau, Seurat (*Le Chahut*), Signac, Toulouse-Lautrec, Van de Velde, Van Rysselberghe, Van Gogh. [Present exhibition nos. 28, 39, 40, 41, 60, 85, 88, 97, 120, 121, 142, and probably 5 and 122.]

Dubois-Pillet dies in August; Lucien Pissarro moves to England, and his father further modifies Neo-Impressionism towards his early style.

1891 Brussels: February, *Les XX:* Angrand, J. Chéret, Walter Crane, Filliger. Finch, Gauguin, Guillaumin, Lemmen, Camille Pissarro, Seurat, Signac (new member), Sisley, Steer, Toorop, Van Gogh (retrospective), Van Rysselberghe, Van de Velde. [Present exhibition nos. 54, 87, 89, 134, 135, and probably 3 and 4.]

Van de Velde very active in Lowlands art circles, begins to change Neo-Impressionism under impact of Van Gogh, and eventually gives up painting for the decorative arts and architecture. Contacts with England, constant since 1885, help increase interest in Arts and Crafts which claims most of Belgian Neo-Impressionists by mid-1890s. Lemmen writes article on Walter Crane, and Finch largely gives up painting for ceramics.

20 March – 27 April: *Indépendants:* Angrand, E. Bernard, P. Bonnard, Cross, M. Denis, Dubois-Pillet (retrospective), Finch, Gausson, Guillaumin, Lemmen, Luce, Petitjean, Lucien Pissarro, Rousseau, Seurat

(*Circus*), Signac, Toulouse-Lautrec, Van de Velde, Van Rysselberghe, Van Gogh (retrospective). [Present exhibition nos. 26, 42, 89, 98, 134, 135.]

Seurat dies of diphtheria during Indépendants exhibition, 31 years and four months old. Hayet, Gausson and Camille Pissarro leave Neo-Impressionism behind, and Lucien Pissarro in England rapidly modifies his manner of painting. Cross, however, does his first mature Neo-Impressionist works, and moves to Mediterranean shore where he will spend the rest of his life. The Nabis, for whom Gauguin is the chosen master, are winning favor among the Symbolists. They, Gauguin and Van Gogh quickly displace the Neo-Impressionists as the dominant artists of the early 1890s.

December: Le Barc de Boutteville holds first of several exhibitions grouping the Nabis and the Neo-Impressionists.

1892 Brussels: February, *Les XX:* M. Cassat, Denis, Finch, Gausson, Lemmen, Luce, Lucien Pissarro, Seurat (retrospective), Toorop, Toulouse-Lautrec, Van Rysselberghe, Van de Velde. [Present exhibition nos. 79, 82, 87, 88, 89, 98, and probably 124.]

Van de Velde and Toorop organize exhibitions for The Hague and Antwerp of French and Belgian artists who habitually show at *Les XX*.

19 March – 27 April: *Indépendants:* Angrand, Bernard, Bonnard, Denis, Gausson, Lemmen, Luce, O'Conor, Petitjean, Lucien Pissarro, Rousseau, Seurat (retrospective), Signac, Toorop, Toulouse-Lautrec, Van Rysselberghe. [Present exhibition nos. 12, 13, 73, 76, 81, 82, 85, 87, 88, 89.]

Seurat retrospective at *La Revue Blanche* as well as at *Les XX* and the *Indépendants*. Signac discovers Saint-Tropez, where later he builds a villa "La Hune".

May and November: Le Barc de Boutteville has second and third exhibitions which include some Neo-Impressionists.

2 December – 8 January: In rented rooms at the Hôtel Brébant, the first exhibition devoted solely to the Neo-Impressionists.

1893 Brussels: February, *Les XX:* Bernard, F. Maddox-Brown, Cross, Finch, Petitjean, Signac, Steer, Thorn-Prikker, Toulouse-Lautrec, Van Rysselberghe, Van de Velde.

> Maria Sèthe, Van Rysselberghe's sister-in-law, and soon to become Van de Velde's wife, is in England as a disciple of William Morris; she brings back to Brussels samples of the work of Morris, Crane and others. Toorop and Finch had frequently visited England, and Lemmen goes there in 1892 and 1894. Shift from Neo-Impressionism to Arts and Crafts and the Art Nouveau is already underway in Lowlands.

Antwerp: *L'Association pour l'Art* includes some Neo-Impressionists in its exhibition.

18 March – 27 April: *Indépendants:* C. Amiet, Angrand, Bonnard, Cross, Denis, Gausson, Laugé, Luce, Petitjean, Lucien Pissarro, Rousseau, A. Séguin, Signac, Steinlen, Toulouse-Lautrec, Van Rysselberghe, L. Valtat.

Galerie Laffitte: With help at first from Antoine de la Rochefoucauld, this shop (later taken over by Léonce Moline) holds many little one-man shows of Neo-Impressionists over the next three years, as well as little group exhibitions.

December – January: Galerie Laffitte: "Groupe des Peintres Néo-Impressionnistes".

1894 Brussels: *La Libre Esthétique* succeeds *Les XX*, maintains same general policies, but Neo-Impressionism beginning to wane. Show includes C. Ashbee, A. Beardsley, E. Carrière, J. Chéret, Denis, Gauguin, Lemmen, Camille and Lucien Pissarro, P. Ranson, Redon, Renoir, Signac, Sisley, Toorop, Toulouse-Lautrec, Van Rysselberghe, G. F. Watts.

> Van de Velde gives frequent lectures in Belgium and Holland on Arts and Crafts, openly admires Morris, Crane and Ruskin. In Brussels, the group "l'Art" is founded by Finch, Lemmen, Van Rysselberghe, Emile Verhaeren and Octave Maus to sponsor the industrial and decorative arts.

Indépendants: Angrand, Cross, Gausson, Laugé, Luce, Petitjean, Lucien Pissarro, Rousseau, Signac, Valtat.

Galerie Laffitte holds second, third and fourth "Groupe des Peintres Néo-Impressionnistes".

1895 Brussels: *La Libre Esthétique:* Ashbee, Beardsley, Chéret, W. Crane, Cross, Denis, Luce, Morren, W. Morris, Camille and Lucien Pissarro, Ranson, Redon, Signac, Toulouse-Lautrec, Vallotton, C. Voysey.

Indépendants: Angrand, Cross, Gausson, G. Lacombe, Petitjean, Rousseau, P. Sérusier, Signac, Van Rysselberghe.

Galerie Laffitte: Exhibition of twenty-four paintings and thirteen drawings by Seurat; one-man show also for Van Rysselberghe.

The Hague: Height of short-lived Hague school of Neo-Impressionists, with J. Aarts, H. P. Bremmer and J. Vijlbrief. Toorop, who had been active in Belgian and Dutch circles since the early 1880s, was in The Hague also and continued to paint landscapes in Neo-Impressionist technique.

December – January: S. Bing opens his "Salon de l'Art Nouveau"; many Neo-Impressionists and Nabis collaborate in exhibition dominated by Van de Velde's designs.

1896 *Indépendants:* Cross, Luce, E. Munch, Petitjean, Rousseau, Signac, L. Valtat.

Angrand leaves Paris for Saint-Laurent-en-Caux in Normandy; since about 1892 has given over painting for drawing.

Galerie Laffitte: Gausson exhibition.

1897 Brussels: *La Libre Esthétique:* Cross, Gauguin, Lemmen, Luce, Monet, Munch, Toorop, Toulouse-Lautrec, C. Voysey.

Finch moves to Finland to teach and make ceramics; remains there rest of life.

Indépendants: Cross, Luce, Munch, Rousseau, Signac, Valtat.

Julius Meier-Graefe, German critic and historian, buys Seurat's *Chahut*, and has Van de Velde make special frame and nearby furniture to suit.

1898 *Indépendants:* Cross, Luce, Signac.

Van Rysselberghe moves to Paris, and eventually to Mediterranean coast near Cross and Signac. Neo-Impressionism no longer represented in Belgium.

Signac's *D'Eugène Delacroix au Néo-Impressionnisme* published first in *La Revue Blanche*, then separately as book; it became the fundamental text on Neo-Impressionism.

In Germany, Count Harry Kessler buys Seurat's *Poseuses;* with Van de Velde's help, he organizes exhibition at Keller and Reiner in Berlin, the first in Germany devoted to Neo-Impressionism. Kessler and Meier-Graefe visit Signac in Paris, arrange for excerpts of his treatise to appear the same year in the German review *Pan*. In Vienna, Van Rysselberghe is included in the *Secession* and almost thirty of his works are reproduced the following year in *Ver Sacrum*, an Austrian art review.

1899 *Indépendants:* Cézanne, Cross, Luce, Signac.

Durand-Ruel gives three rooms to the Neo-Impressionists and the Nabis; he also gives Luce a one-man show.

Matisse's first flirtation with Neo-Impressionist technique.

1900 *Indépendants:* Luce, J. Puy, Signac.

Seurat given large retrospective by *La Revue Blanche*.

1901 *Indépendants:* Angrand, Bonnard, Cézanne, L. Cousturier, Cross, Denis, Ensor, Lacombe, Lemmen, Luce, A. Marquet, Matisse, Petitjean, Puy, Ranson, K. X. Roussel, Van Rysselberghe, Sérusier, Signac, Vallotton, Valtat, Vuillard.

Berlin: Keller and Reiner show Neo-Impressionists regularly.

1902 *Indépendants:* Bernard, Bonnard, Cézanne, Cousturier, Cross, Denis, Toulouse-Lautrec (retrospective), Lemmen, Luce, Manguin, Marquet, Matisse, Petitjean, Puy, Roussel, Signac, Vallotton, Valtat, Van Rysselberghe, Vuillard.

Signac exhibition at Bing's, and Van Rysselberghe at the Maison des Artistes.

In Germany, Van de Velde, Count Kessler, Meier-Graefe and Curt Herrmann help organize a number of exhibitions of Neo-Impressionism beginning this year; they correspond regularly with Signac and Cross, and have the assistance of Félix Fénéon in borrowing and purchasing paintings. Hagen, Weimar and Berlin are centers for collections of Neo-Impressionism being formed. Curt Herrmann and Christian Rohlfs join Paul Baum as Neo-Impressionists; later others will work in the new style: A. Deuber, I. Hauptmann, W. Morgner, H. Olde, W. Ophey, W. Schmurr.

1903 *Indépendants:* Angrand, Bonnard, C. Camoin, Cousturier, Cross, Denis, R. Dufy, O. Friesz, Luce, Manguin, Marquet, Matisse, J. Metzinger, Munch, O'Conor, Petitjean, F. Picabia, Puy, Roussel, Signac, Vallotton, Van Rysselberghe, Vuillard.

Still more of future Fauves and Cubists than previous year now show with Signac, Cross and the *Indépendants.*

Druet opens new gallery and exhibits Neo-Impressionists almost continuously until 1914.

Salon d'Automne has first exhibition; will become principal home of Fauves, but they will also regularly show with *Indépendants.*

In Germany related exhibitions in Berlin, Weimar, Hamburg and other cities feature Baum, Herrmann and Rohlfs alongside Angrand, Cross, Luce, Signac and Van Rysselberghe. Herrmann's wife publishes translation of Signac's *D'Eugène Delacroix au Néo-Impressionnisme,* and Signac is given one-man show at Cassirer's, in Berlin.

1904 *Indépendants:* Bonnard, Camoin, Cousturier, Cross, R. Delaunay, Denis, Dufy, Friesz, Lemmen, Luce, Manguin, Marquet, Matisse, Metzinger, Munch, O'Conor, Petitjean, Puy, Roussel, Sérusier, Signac, Vallotton, Valtat, Van Dongen, Van Rysselberghe, Vuillard.

Early phase of Fauvism characterized by strong Neo-Impressionist current. Signac and Cross are host to many of future Fauves in their Mediterranean villas; Matisse spends summer with Signac, and has Neo-Impressionist period lasting a year and a half. Derain has a similar period of about two years, and Metzinger and Delaunay will maintain a mosaic-Neo-Impressionism for several years longer.

Signac and Luce exhibitions at Druet.

Brussels: *La Libre Esthétique* has major retrospective of Impressionism and Neo-Impressionism. A similar exhibition organized in Helsinki by Finch, the first such show in Finland. Several Neo-Impressionists are included in the *Phalanx* exhibition in Munich.

1905 *Indépendants:* Angrand, Bernard, Bonnard, Camoin, Cousturier, Cross, C. Herrmann, Delaunay, Denis, A. Derain, Dufy, Friesz, K. Kollwitz, Lacombe, Le Fauconnier, Lemmen, Luce, Manguin, Marquet, Matisse, Metzinger, Munch, O'Conor, Petitjean, Puy, G. Rouault, Roussel, Sérusier, Seurat (retrospective), Signac, Vallotton, Valtat, Van Dongen, Van Gogh (retrospective), Van Rysselberghe, Vlaminck, Vuillard.

Cross and Van Rysselberghe have shows at Druet.

Fauvism is publicly baptized at the Salon d'Automne, with Matisse as the leading figure.

In Italy, a few painters flirt with Neo-Impressionism, but only Pellizza da Volpedo makes important essays in the French style, and Severini later, after his move to Paris in 1906. Italian Divisionism was essentially independent of Neo-Impressionism, but in the period before the war, some interaction takes place in the work of V. Grubicy de Dragon, G. Marussy, P. Mengarini, V. Meoni, A. Noci and P. Nomellini.

1906 *Indépendants:* Angrand, Bernard, Bonnard, G. Braque, Camoin, Cousturier, Cross, Delaunay, Denis, Derain, Dufy, Friesz, A. Herbin, Lacombe, Laugé, M. Laurencin, Le Fauconnier, F. Léger, Lemmen, Luce, Manguin, Marquet, Matisse, Metzinger, Munch, O'Conor, Petitjean, Puy, Roussel, Sérusier, Signac, Vallotton, Valtat, Van Dongen, Van Rysselberghe, Vlaminck, Vuillard.

The largest assemblage to date of Neo-Impressionists, Fauves and future Cubists. Although Matisse is already beyond his Neo-Impressionist period, most of the others use divided color or mosaic brushwork.

Luce exhibition at Druet.

Brussels: *La Libre Esthétique* invites Matisse, Manguin, Camoin and other Fauves through intercession of Van Rysselberghe.
Berlin: Curt Herrmann organizes a Neo-Impressionist section of the *Secession*.

Exhibition of "Französische Künstler", with Neo-Impressionists given principal representation, travels to

Munich, Frankfurt, Dresden, Karlsruhe and Stuttgart.

1907 Bernheim-Jeune gives one-man shows to Signac, Cross and Luce.

Salon d'Automne: Maus (secretary of La Libre Esthétique) organizes Belgian section for the Paris exhibition.

Krefeld: "Exposition d'Art Français" includes Neo-Impressionists.

1908 Bernheim-Jeune gives one-man show to Van Rysselberghe, and major retrospective to Seurat.

Meister der Farbe, Leipzig review, devotes issue to Neo-Impressionists, including Paul Baum.

1909 Druet holds exhibition of Neo-Impressionist drawings and watercolors.

Bernheim-Jeune has Luce exhibition.

In Holland, Mondrian uses a mosaic divisionism, probably resulting from contact with Toorop who maintains a Neo-Impressionist technique for landscapes.

1910 Death of Cross; memorial exhibition at Bernheim-Jeune.

Luce exhibition at Bernheim-Jeune.

In England, exhibitions of modern French artists at the Public Art Galleries, Brighton, and the Grafton Galleries, London, include Neo-Impressionists.

The Italian Divisionist Gaetano Previati publishes his *Scientific Principles of Divisionism*, a color treatise based on Neo-Impressionist theory.

1911 Signac and Cross exhibitions at Bernheim-Jeune, and in Brussels at *La Libre Esthétique*, another Cross retrospective.

At the *Indépendants*, to which Signac and Cross (until his death) contributed every year, the famous "Salle 41", the room in which the young Cubists exhibited together.

Second edition of Signac's *D'Eugène Delacroix au Néo-Impressionnisme*.

Publication in Germany of Curt Herrmann's *Der*

Kampf um den Stil, a manifesto owing much to Neo-Impressionist theories.

Beginning of particular importance of Seurat's work among the Cubists and Futurists, especially his late paintings *Le Chahut* and *The Circus*, available in Druet and other reproductions.

1920 Beginning of Le Corbusier's and Ozenfant's *L'Esprit Nouveau*, the organ of Purism, which gives major place to Seurat and has articles by Charles Henry.

1921 Appearance of Severini's *Du Cubisme au Classicisme*, which draws upon Henry's and Signac's writings; one of many essays by artists (Lhote, Gleizes, Hélion) who regard Seurat's "classicism" as the only major heritage of Neo-Impressionism.

1927 Lyon: Salon du Sud-Est incorporates "Rétrospective de l'Epoque Néo-Impressionniste".

1932 Braun: "Le Néo-Impressionnisme".

1933 Beaux-Arts: "Seurat et ses Amis", the most comprehensive exhibition of French Neo-Impressionism ever held.

1935 Death of Signac.

1936 Bolette Natanson: "Peintures de la *Revue Blanche*".

Rotterdam, Museum Boymans (winter 1936–1937): "De Divisionisten van Georges Seurat tot Jan Toorop": Until 1968, the only retrospective of Neo-Impressionism in a public museum.

1937 London: Wildenstein, "Seurat and his Contemporaries".

Zürich: Aktuaryus, "Le Néo-Impressionnisme".

1942 Galerie de France (winter 1942–1943): "Les Néo-Impressionnistes".

1943 John Rewald's *Seurat* published in New York, first substantial account of early Neo-Impressionism.

1950 New London, Connecticut, Lyman Allen Museum: "From Delacroix to the Neo-Impressionists".

London: Redfern, "The Pointillists and their Period".

1952 Venice Biennale has retrospective section "Il
Divisionismo" including French painters.

1953 New York: Wildenstein, "Seurat and his Friends".

1954 Galerie Baugin: "Autour de Seurat".

1955 *Indépendants:* "Hommage à Paul Signac et ses Amis".

1956   John Rewald's *Post-Impressionism from Van Gogh
to Gauguin*, with history of early Neo-Impressionism
that remains the standard text.

1958 Saint-Denis, Musée Municipal d'Histoire et d'Art:
"Luce et les Néo-Impressionnistes".

1960 André Maurice: "Les Néo-Impressionnistes".

1961 J. C. and J. Bellier: "Les Néo-Impressionnistes".

1962 New York: Hammer, "Seurat and his Friends".

Brussels, Musées Royaux, and Otterlo, Rijksmuseum
Kröller-Müller: "Le Groupe des XX et son Temps"
gives important place to Neo-Impressionists.

1963 André Maurice: "Néo-Impressionnisme".

New York: Hirschl and Adler, "Neo-Impressionism".

1965 *Indépendants:* "Les Premiers Indépendants
1884–1894": most Neo-Impressionists included.

New Haven, Yale University Art Gallery: "Neo-
Impressionists and Nabis in the collection of Arthur
G. Altschul."

1966 *Indépendants:* "Les Indépendants à la Belle Epoque
1895–1901" includes many Neo-Impressionists.

Brussels, Musées Royaux: "Evocation des 'XX' et de
'La Libre Esthétique'" includes Belgian and French
Neo-Impressionists.

London: Arthur Tooth and Sons, "Pointillisme".

1967 Hervé: "Quelques Tableaux de Maîtres Néo-
Impressionnistes".

BIBLIOGRAPHY

1 REWALD, John. *Post-Impressionism from van Gogh to Gauguin*, Museum of Modern Art, 1956 et seq. Pride of place must be given to Rewald's monumental history, covering the crucial years of Neo-Impressionism from 1886 to 1891; critical bibliographies remain indispensable.

2 SUTTER, Jean (ed.). *Les Néo-Impressionnistes*. Paris, 1968 [in press]. Biographies, with a remarkable amount of new information, by J. Sutter, P. Angrand, I. Compin, L. Bazalgette, P. Eberhart, A. Fern, H. Certigny, and C. Fryns, of Seurat, Angrand, Cross, Dubois-Pillet, Luce, Hayet, Gausson, Petitjean, Signac and others.

3 ANGRAND, Pierre. *Naissance des Artistes Indépendants 1884*. Paris, 1965. The best summary of the "Indépendants", the exhibition society central to the history of Neo-Impressionism.

4 BRUSSELS, MUSEES ROYAUX DES BEAUX-ARTS DE BELGIQUE and OTTERLO, RIJKSMUSEUM KRÖLLER-MÜLLER (A. M. Hammacher and F. C. Legrand, eds.). *Le Groupe des XX et son temps*. 17 February – 31 May 1962. With its excellent capsule biographies and bibliographies, one of the best sources for the study of Neo-Impressionism in Belgium.

5 CACHIN, Françoise (ed.). *Félix Fénéon, Au-delà de l'impressionnisme*. Paris, Miroirs de l'Art series, 1966. Superb and well documented introduction, excellent choice of texts of Neo-Impressionism's principal critic.

6 CACHIN, Françoise (ed.). *Paul Signac, D'Eugène Delacroix au néo-impressionnisme*. Paris, Miroirs de l'Art series, 1964. Like the former, a superb introduction to a fundamental text.

7 HALBERTSMA, K. J. A. *A History of the Theory of Color*. Amsterdam, 1949. Probably the best general history of color theory in the nineteenth century.

8 HERBERT, Eugenia W. *The Artist and Social Reform*. New Haven, 1961. Together with the following article, discusses relationships between social ideals and art of French and Belgian Neo-Impressionists.

9 HERBERT, Robert L. and Eugenia W. "Artists and Anarchism, Unpublished Letters of Pissarro, Signac and Others", *Burlington Magazine*, vol. 102, no. 692, November 1960, pp. 473–482, and no. 693, December 1960, pp. 517–522.

10 HOMER, William I. *Seurat and the Science of Painting.* Cambridge, 1964. Deals principally with Chevreul, Rood, Henry and other scientists Seurat consulted; explanations of scientific color theory often given for own sake and not related to painting, but of basic value for Neo-Impressionism.

11 KAHN, Gustave. "Au temps de Pointillisme", *Mercure de France*, vol. 171, 1 April 1924, pp. 5–23. Major text relating Seurat and Neo-Impressionism to Symbolist literature by one of the painter's principal friends.

12 LOOSJES-TERPSTRA, A. B. *Moderne Kunst in Nederland 1900–1914.* Utrecht, 1958, revised and enlarged, 1959. The fundamental study of the period in the Netherlands, with excellent bibliographies and tables for the Dutch Neo-Impressionists.

13 MARET, François [i.e., Franz van Ermengen]. *Les Peintres Luministes.* Brussels, 1944. One of the most intelligent summaries of Neo-Impressionism and color theory.

14 MAUS, Madeleine Octave. *Trente années de lutte pour l'Art, 1884–1914.* Brussels, 1926. Richly documented history of "Les XX" and "La Libre Esthétique", the two exhibition societies principally involved in the history of Neo-Impressionism in Belgium.

15 NEW HAVEN, YALE UNIVERSITY ART GALLERY (R. L. Herbert, ed.). *Neo-Impressionists and Nabis in the collection of Arthur G. Altschul.* 20 January – 14 March 1965. Essential lists of exhibitions, major events and bibliographies.

16 NIEMEYER, Wilhelm. *Malerische Impression und koloristischer Rhythmus.* Düsseldorf, 1920. Traces Neo-Impressionism into Germany, discusses many minor German artists.

17 PARIS, MUSEE DU LOUVRE (M. T. Lemoyne de Forges, ed.). *Signac.* December 1963 – February 1964. Extensive commentaries and texts go beyond Signac to document the whole period.

18 PARIS, SOCIETE DES ARTISTES INDEPENDANTS. *Trente ans d'Art Indépendant, 1884–1914.* 1926. Memorial catalogue with appendices that record pictures exhibited by the Neo-Impressionists.

19 WEBSTER, J. Carson. "The Technique of Impressionism, a Reappraisal", *College Art Journal*, vol. IV, no. 4, November 1944, pp. 3–22. An indispensable application of common sense to color theory and artistic practice.

20 ANGRAND heirs, Paris. Letters from Signac, Cross, van Rysselberghe and others; extensive file of annotated catalogues, press clippings and articles from periodicals; preliminary catalogue of Angrand's oeuvre.

21 BIBLIOTHEQUE DOUCET, Paris. Miscellaneous letters and documents concerning Fénéon and others.

22 LUCE heirs, Paris. Letters from Angrand, Cross, Signac and others.

23 SIGNAC heirs, Paris. The richest corpus of documents for the period, including letters from Angrand, Cross, Dubois-Pillet, Hayet, Luce, Camille Pissarro, Seurat, Fénéon and many others; incorporates Cross archives and part of Fénéon archives as well.

24 VAN RYSSELBERGHE heirs, France. Letters from Angrand, Cross, Luce, Camille Pissarro, Signac and others.

25 LEMMEN heirs, Brussels. Letters, diaries and notebooks of Lemmen.

26 LES XX, LA LIBRE ESTHETIQUE, OCTAVE MAUS archives, in the Archives de l'Art Contemporain (Musées Royaux), Brussels. Maus was the secretary of Les XX and its successor La Libre Esthétique; his very rich archives include letters from Cézanne, Rodin, Seurat and innumerable others, and extensive documentation for the exhibitions in Brussels from 1884 to 1914. These are being classified and edited by Mmes. F. C. Legrand, M. J. Chartrain-Hebbelinck and Ph. Mertens, and some were published in the *Bulletin* of the Musées Royaux, 1966, nos. 1–2.

27 VAN DE VELDE archives, in the Bibliothèque Royale de Belgique, Brussels. Thousands of letters from the Neo-Impressionist painters and others; personal manuscripts of Henry Van de Velde; for the history of Neo-Impressionism, second only to the Signac archives; for the general history of art of the period, second to none. Papers have been classified by Mme. C. Lemaire.

28 VERHAEREN archives, in the Bibliothèque Royale de Belgique, Brussels. Emile Verhaeren's literary estate, including letters from Seurat, Signac and many other Neo-Impressionists.

29 LUCIEN PISSARRO archives, Pissarro heirs, Oxford, England. Although drawn upon already by John Rewald, these materials are still rich in unpublished letters from Dubois-Pillet, Hayet, Signac, Van de Velde and others, and the journals of Lucien's wife Esther are of collateral interest, especially in the years before 1895.

PHOTOGRAPHIC CREDITS

Kenny Strattman, Indianapolis, Indiana: no. 111
Soichi Sunami, New York: no. 169
The Tate Gallery, London: no. 117
Taylor and Dull, New York: nos. 27, 45
The Toledo Museum of Art, Toledo, Ohio: no. 104
Charles Uht, New York: no. 127
"Velay" photo, Le Puy, France: no. 28
Victoria National Gallery, Melbourne, Australia: no. 90
Jean Willemin, Paris: nos. 3, 4, 9, 11, 131
A. J. Wyatt, Philadelphia: no. 116
Yale University Art Gallery, New Haven: no. 118

Color plates were lent by:
Fonds Mercator, Brussels: no. 142
The Museum of Modern Art, New York: no. 168
Rijksmuseum Kröller-Müller, Otterlo: no. 93
Skira International Corporation, Geneva: nos. 27, 76, 82, 86

TABLE OF CONTENTS

Exhibition 68/1   February 1968 — April 1968

5,000 copies of this catalogue designed by Arthur S. Congdon have been printed by Brüder Rosenbaum, Vienna in January 1968 for the Trustees of The Solomon R. Guggenheim Foundation on the occasion of the loan exhibition "Neo-Impressionism"